WILD MAMMALS
OF VIRGINIA

WILD MAMMALS OF VIRGINIA

By

CHARLES O. HANDLEY, Jr.

and

CLYDE P. PATTON

A contribution of the Virginia Cooperative Wildlife Research Unit: the Commission of Game and Inland Fisheries, the Virginia Polytechnic Institute, the Wildlife Management Institute, and the United States Fish and Wildlife Service, cooperating.

Published by

COMMONWEALTH OF VIRGINIA

COMMISSION OF GAME AND INLAND FISHERIES

7 North Second Street

RICHMOND, VIRGINIA

1947

COMMONWEALTH OF VIRGINIA

WILLIAM M. TUCK, *Governor*

COMMISSION OF GAME AND INLAND FISHERIES

COMMISSIONERS

BEVERLY W. STRAS, JR., *Chairman*

CHARLES D. ANDREWS   THOMAS G. HERRING

ERNEST C. MEAD   WARREN B. RAINS

E. C. NETTLES   WM. S. SNOW

FRANK P. BURTON   FRANK C. WILEY

EVELYN M. PARIS, *Secretary*

GENERAL STAFF

I. T. QUINN, *Executive Director*

M. D. HART, *Executive Secretary*

G. W. BULLER, *Chief, Fish Division*

CHESTER F. PHELPS, *Chief, Game Division*

CLYDE P. PATTON, *Chief, Publications Division*

LILLIAN B. LAYNE, *Chief, Accounts and Licensing Division*

PREFACE

In recent years much effort has been exerted by research workers to establish a system of management for game animals which will aid in restoring these species to depleted areas in the State. To aid them in faunal problems involving the distribution of both harmful and valuable species of mammals, the Virginia Cooperative Wildlife Research Unit undertook as one of its first major projects a study of the distribution of Virginia mammals, and granted C. P. Patton a fellowship to conduct the study. Later the study was continued and enlarged by C. O. Handley, Jr., and others, and the final results are presented in this publication.

As may be seen from the text and from the accompanying distribution maps, much yet remains to be learned about the distribution of most Virginia mammals. This publication is only a beginning; a foundation upon which more comprehensive and more complete works may be based. Its purpose is to put into the hands of the farmer, the hunter, the student, and the teacher, a simple, adequate reference that will help him fill in the numerous gaps in our knowledge.

With the aid of the simple keys and the more detailed descriptions, one should be able to identify with a fair degree of certainty almost any mammal which might chance to come into his hands. If the identification is not certain, or if it is suspected that the animal is of a rare kind, an endeavor should be made to preserve the specimen. In all cases, the skull should be saved, for often the animal can be identified from its skull alone.

The Virginia Cooperative Wildlife Research Unit has for several years been preparing a collection of Virginia mammals, and specimens from all sources are gladly accepted and much appreciated. Also, correspondence which may lead to a better understanding of the distribution of Virginia mammals is invited.

During their distributional study, the authors personally collected and preserved as museum specimens approximately 750 specimens of Virginia mammals, most of which were deposited in the Virginia Cooperative Wildlife Research Unit Museum at Blacksburg, and in the University of Michigan Museum of Zoology

(iii)

at Ann Arbor, Michigan. In order to secure additional records of museum specimens, an examination was made of the collection of the Academy of Natural Sciences of Philadelphia and of the U. S. National Museum collections. Through correspondence it was learned that Virginia material was contained also in the American Museum of Natural History, New York; the Charleston Museum, Charleston, South Carolina; and the Carnegie Museum, Pittsburgh, Pennsylvania. The specimens in these institutions were not examined by the authors, but are indicated on the distributional maps as specimens reported. Numerous other specimens were examined in the Virginia Mineral, Timber and Historical Museum, Richmond, and in the University of Virginia collections at the Mountain Lake Biological Station and the Seward Forest, Triplet, Virginia. The Economic Wildlife Investigations Section, U. S. Fish and Wildlife Service, has collected a number of mammals from the State for use in their reference collections, and their analyses of the stomachs of reptiles, birds, and mammals taken in Virginia have also yielded many records of various species of mammals. Altogether the authors have examined more than 3,000 specimens of Virginia mammals.

CHARLES O. HANDLEY, Sr., *Leader*
VIRGINIA COOPERATIVE WILDLIFE
RESEARCH UNIT

ACKNOWLEDGMENTS

The authors wish to express their grateful acknowledgment for the assistance and inspiration given by C. O. Handley, Leader, Virginia Cooperative Wildlife Research Unit, under whose supervision this publication was prepared.

We are also greatly indebted to W. H. Burt and E. T. Hooper for unlimited use of the collections at the University of Michigan Museum of Zoology and for many valuable suggestions on the manuscript; to Gustav Swanson of the Fish and Wildlife Service for valuable criticisms and suggestions on the manuscript; to H. H. T. Jackson and the late A. H. Howell of the Fish and Wildlife Service for identifying study material and the use of specimens from the Biological Survey collection; to G. S. Miller for use of the U. S. National Museum Mammal collection; to Remington Kellogg for assistance in locating records of aquatic mammals contained in the U. S. National Museum and for checking the manuscript; to A. L. Nelson for the use of the records and study material at the Patuxent Research Refuge; and to the late Wharton Huber for the use of the collection of the Academy of Natural Sciences of Philadelphia. We express our thanks to I. D. Wilson, A. B. Massey, and C. F. DeLaBarre, of the Virginia Polytechnic Institute Department of Biology, for helpful suggestions and assistance offered throughout the course of the study; to J. B. Lewis for collection of specimens and much invaluable information on mammals of southeastern Virginia; to L. S. Givens, A. B. Culbertson, W. B. McIntosh, L. M. Llewellyn, W. R. DeGarmo, and others for assistance in collecting study material; to the many correspondents who sent in valuable information; and to those agencies which contributed illustrative material.

CONTENTS

INTRODUCTION

Before we can begin to speak seriously on any subject we must first have a basic understanding of the subject and its essentials. Before we begin to consider the mammals of Virginia then, we should first understand their relationships with other animals and the system by which they are classified. We should also know what a mammal is and how to tell it from all other animals.

The classification of mammals, and for that matter all living organisms, is based on a careful study of their relationships to one another. Objects on the earth are divided into two great groups: those things which have never had life, have never reproduced their kind, never breathed, nor assimilated food—those things which are **inorganic**; and those things which have lived, reproduced, breathed, and taken food—those things which are **organic**. These organic beings are in turn segregated into the **Plant Kingdom**, consisting of organisms which manufacture their own food within their bodies by means of chlorophyl and which are more or less stationary; and into the **Animal Kingdom**, which consists of organisms not capable of producing food within their bodies, and usually not stationary.

In the animal kingdom there are several large divisions called phyla. Among the phyla are the protozoa, sponges, jelly-fish, flat-worms, round worms, annelid worms, mollusks, starfish, insects, and chordates. It is the **Phylum Chordata** which we are interested in, since here are found the vertebrate animals, or **Subphylum Vertebrata**. All the other phyla are made up of invertebrate animals—animals without backbones. Classed among the vertebrates are the amphibians, the fishes, the reptiles, the birds, and the mammals. The mammals are the **Class Mammalia**.

To distinguish mice and squirrels and deer from all other animals we call them mammals. Mammals are animals with warm blood, a four-chambered heart, hairy bodies, mammary glands, and highly developed brains. Among the members of the vast animal kingdom, only the birds share with the mammals the characteristic of warm blood which remains at a definite temperature, while the blood of other animals varies with the temperature of their surroundings. Only birds and mammals have the heart divided into two auricles and two ventricles. Other animals have three cham-

1

bers, two chambers, or no true heart at all. Although some mammals such as certain of the dolphins and seals appear to be quite hairless, a closer inspection will reveal hairs on some part of their bodies. The presence of mammary glands and the nursing of young are characteristics found nowhere in the animal kingdom except among the mammals. While anatomy reveals many other characteristics peculiar to mammals alone, the ones we have mentioned are the most conspicuous.

In the preceding paragraphs we have shown how mammals are distinguished from other animals of the world. We have discussed the classification of the animal kingdom down to class, and presently we shall continue the discussion to the ultimates of species and subspecies. The meaning of classification should now be evident. It is merely a means of grouping like organisms together because of their similarities. Naturally, at the top of the classification where all organisms are separated into two kingdoms, the degree of likeness between any two members of a kingdom may be only remote, so to lump like with like and to separate like from unlike we split the kingdom into phyla, and then for the same reasons split the phyla into classes. The further we split, the more alike the animals we class together become.

The Class Mammalia is separated into three subclasses according to the method by which the young are borne. The most ancient of the mammals, the egg-laying **Protheria** of Australia, are a connecting link between modern mammals and their reptilian ancestors. Next in line are the **Metatheria,** mostly Australian, in which the young are born in a very immature state with never a placental attachment to the mother. The only North American representatives of this primitive group are the opossums. All modern mammals belong to the subclass **Eutheria,** in which the young are nourished by means of a placenta in prenatal life, and it is with this group that we shall be mostly concerned in this book.

The subclass Eutheria is divided into nine orders, and to differentiate further, the orders are divided into families, the families into genera, and the genera into species. These divisions may be better appreciated by examining the systematic catalog. The species stand at the very bottom of the classification system for they are the finest point of division. A species may be divided into geographic races or subspecies, but they are the same animal, not distinct from one another as was the case with the phylum and class, or class and order.

All this system of modern classification was devised in 1758 by a Swede named Carl Linnaeus. At the same time he gave each organism an international name, a name which would have the same meaning for a German or a Russian or an American as it would for a Swede. This Latin or Latinized Greek name is called a "scientific name." Each scientific name consists of two or three parts. The first part is the name of the genus or general group to which the organism belongs; the second is the name of the species; and the third, if there is a third, is the subspecies. Thus, the common chipmunk of Virginia in scientific terminology is called *Tamias striatus fisheri*. This name indicates that it is a mammal of the genus *Tamias* and the species *striatus*, with the local variety being *fisheri*. In Virginia *Tamias striatus* is known variously as chipmunk, ground squirrel, and gopher. In other sections of the country these names refer to entirely different animals, so if a person were talking to someone from another section of the country, neither could be sure just what sort of an animal the other was talking about. If they had used the scientific name, *Tamias striatus*, there could have been no confusion, since of the millions of living organisms in the world only one is known by the name *Tamias striatus*.

In the latter portion of this book, beginning on page 99, will be found a technical classification of the mammals of Virginia where strict scientific nomenclature has been used, but in the pages immediately following another plan has been employed. Here the mammals are classified and discussed according to their relationship to man, rather than according to their relationships with each other. For this discussion the mammals are grouped as game, furbearers, rodents, insectivorous, marine, and vanished. While this grouping is not strictly scientific, it will lend appeal to the average reader.

STUDYING VIRGINIA MAMMALS

When people go out for an afternoon stroll, if they notice anything at all besides the physical aspects of the scenery, it is usually the birds and the wild flowers. They are such conspicuous parts of the living scenery that they can be observed and studied with ease. Most mammals, on the other hand, are so inconspicuous that they are ordinarily overlooked by the casual observer. Of course, some species like the squirrels and the rabbit and the skunk are familiar to everyone because of certain characteristic habits, but most species are relatively unknown.

At least part of this unfamiliarity may be overcome by learning where to look for mammals and what to look for. The well-beaten trails of meadow mice can almost always be found in damp meadows by parting the thick grass or by raising the mat of dead vegetation covering the ground, and sharp eyes will often discover the mice scurrying along their trails. Small piles of cut grass stems are another sure sign of mice, and small globular masses of dried grasses with a lining of moss are mouse nests. In the forests, mouse nests and runways may be found beneath stones and in or under rotting logs, and by carefully removing the leafy layer on the forest floor, networks of mouse runways may often be found. Quietness and stealth are frequently rewarded with glimpses of mammals along woodland trails.

Tracks of mice, as well as the larger mammals, may be observed in soft mud along creeks and in ditches, but winter observations during snowy periods offer many more possibilities in the study of tracks. Careful observation of tracks and trails at this season often reveals fascinating stories written in the snow.

To become familiar with bats requires visits to caves or little frequented attics, or patient observation in their favorite hunting areas, as along roads or over ponds. Marine mammals may sometimes be observed from beaches and at times the tidal wash brings ashore specimens which become stranded.

No matter how carefully field observations are made, familiarity with small mammals may be gained only by handling specimens. Trapping must be resorted to. The ordinary commercial mouse trap is fine for mice and shrews, although the slightly larger "museum special" trap is better for careful work. The commercial rat trap is the thing to use for the various kinds of rats, and properly used may catch moles, which are best caught though in traps especially designed for the purpose. Small traps using the spring door principle may be easily designed to obtain specimens alive. Traps should be baited with damp oatmeal or pieces of bacon and placed in runways or at the entrances of burrows.

To prepare study skins of specimens caught, the following procedure should be followed: First of all determine the sex of the animal if possible. In certain of the shrews this may be difficult. Next, certain measurements should be taken including the total length from the tip of the nose to the tip of the tail bone, the length of the tail from the tip of the bone to where the tail joins the backbone, and the length of the hind foot from the heel to the tip of the longest toenail. This information should be noted on a tag along with the locality of trapping, date, and collector, and should be fastened to a hind leg of the completed specimen (Fig. 1).

No special experience in taxidermy is needed to prepare usable and valuable mammal study specimens, for in a study specimen, a lifelike pose is not necessary. The body of the specimen is removed through a slit in the belly, and the skin is then stuffed with cotton and pinned on a board to dry. The American Museum of Natural History, New York, has prepared an excellent and inex-

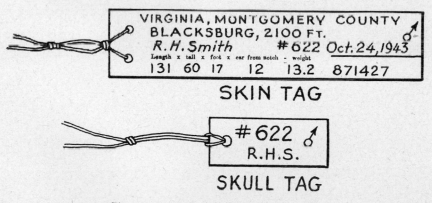

Fig. 1.—Properly labeled specimen tags.

pensive booklet on the preparation of mammal study skins. Along with the skin, the skull should be saved, for it is important in identification. The specimen should be given a number, and the same number should be noted on both the skull and specimen tags so that the two cannot become separated. Thus preserved, the specimen can be studied at leisure and if necessary may later be identified at a museum.

In the following chapters will be found information on the habits and homes of mammals which may aid in observation, and in the last chapter a systematic catalog is provided as an aid in the identification of specimens.

GAME MAMMALS

It seems only logical to begin the discussion of the mammals of Virginia with those mammals which are both the most conspicuous and the most important economically to us. Not only do the game mammals furnish sport and recreation and priceless trophies to the hunter, but also meat and often valuable fur.

The small game mammals are probably more numerous today than they were when Virginia belonged to the Indians, but the larger mammals have suffered terribly from the inroads of civilization. The buffalo is gone; the elk disappeared and was brought back; the bear is hated and destroyed wherever it appears; and the deer, although increasing, is persecuted wherever it lives near the haunts of man.

According to Seton (1929)[1], the first identifiable record of **deer** in Virginia was made by Thomas Hariot who visited this territory in 1584. In his account of the colony he said: "Of Beastes. Deare in some places there are great store: neere unto the sea-coast they are of the ordinarie bignes as ours in England, and some lesse: but further vp into the countrye where there is better feed, they are greater: they differ from ours onely in this, their tailes are longer, and the snags of their hornes looke backward." (Quaritch Reprint 1893 p. 29.)

Apparently the next mention of deer in Virginia was made by Captain John Smith when early in the seventeenth century, according to Arber (1910), he wrote: "Of beasts the chief are Deare, nothing different from ours. In the deserts towards the heads of rivers, ther(e) are many, but amongst the rivers few." Beverly (1722) mentioned the occurrence of deer in Virginia, and Boyd (1929) gave many instances of deer being killed by William Byrd along the Virginia-North Carolina dividing line in 1728. Quoting an incident from Byrd's diary which told of killing two brace of deer, he wrote: "We only primed the deer, being unwilling to be encumbered with whole carcasses. The rest we consigned to the wolves which in return serenaded us a great part of the night." George Washington, at Mount Vernon, Fairfax County, in his

[1]Publications referred to parenthetically by date are listed in the Bibliography, page 207.

7

diary for the latter part of the eighteenth century made frequent mention of his fox hounds being sidetracked on a deer chase. Audubon and Bachman (1846-1854) writing of deer said: "In the mountainous portions of Virginia it is hunted with success." According to Wayland (1912), an article in *The Register* (Nov. 29, 1877) contained the following about the hunting experiences of the late James Todd of Rockingham County: "He was the most remarkable hunter in the Valley of Virginia, having killed over 2700 deer up to 1860, with one muzzle loading rifle...."

Among our big game mammals perhaps none is better known than the deer, for thanks to wise conservation and restocking programs, it now occurs commonly in at least 89 of Virginia's 100 counties. Given proper protection it is one of the easiest mammals to reintroduce into areas from which it has disappeared, and it even thrives in captivity with little more care than is usually afforded the common domesticated animals.

During the early part of the century deer disappeared from all the mountain counties except Craig, Alleghany, Bath, and Highland along the Alleghany Backbone where they continued to thrive in considerable numbers in the best remaining mountain wilderness area in the State. Elsewhere fire, man, and their worst enemy, the roving, self hunting dog, had finished off the last of the native deer. The fire menace was largely removed by the fire protection system established in the early 'thirties, but still the dog was a stumbling-block. Because of dogs the initial restocking program met with only limited success, and it was only because of the establishment of wise dog laws in most sections that later restocking can be hailed as almost universally successful. In 1945, for the first time in almost 50 years, sportsmen again enjoyed deer hunting in southwest Virginia, a region which barely ten years before had been almost devoid of deer. Wise conservation measures always pay off with dividends.

Deer have always been common in the tidewater sections of the State where they find ample protection in the river swamps, and recently in counties south of the James they have become so numerous that their depredations on the peanut and soybean fields have necessitated the opening of the season on does in order to reduce the overabundant population. In this region deer are said to be larger and have more beautiful antlers than anywhere else in the South.

Indeed, there are only two southern heads among the thirty-five largest white-tailed deer heads recorded for North America in the book of the Boone and Crockett Club, "North American Big Game," 1939. One of these was from Texas and the other from Surry County, Virginia. The lengths of the antlers of the Texas deer were longer (27-11/16 & 27-9/16 as against 27-5/16 & 26-7/16, respectively); but the antlers of the Virginia specimen, killed in 1936 by Tom Barclay, were heavier (circumference of main beam: 4-5/8 & 4-7/16 as against 3-3/4 & 3-15/16 in the Texas specimen), and the spread was greater (24-3/16 as against 23-5/16). All measurements are in inches.

Because of its secretive and skulking habits, deer can live successfully very close to civilization, and there is no good reason why they shouldn't eventually occur again in every county of the State.

In more northern regions deep snows force deer to band together into "yards" for the winter season, but in Virginia they are free ranging the year around. Their winter food consists mostly of twigs and buds, browsed from both deciduous and coniferous trees and shrubs. Acorns are another important item. Their natural foods in summer are grass and succulent herbs, and buds and tender leaves of low bushes. They are very fond of salt, and both natural and artificial salt licks are a great attraction to them. Where deer are overabundant or where outlying fields extend into their territory, they may develop an unfortunate fondness for peas, lettuce, young corn or peanuts, and since healthy deer can easily negotiate a seven-foot fence, fences are no hindrance to a hungry deer.

The little spotted fawns which are born late in the spring are among the most beautiful of our wild creatures, and there is little wonder that many of them are picked up each year by well-meaning citizens who believe them to be foundlings. Actually in most cases their mothers are nearby, and though it may not seem so at the time, it is cruel to separate the little animal from its mother. Fawns are very easily raised on a bottle, and after they are weaned they even thrive on table scraps, but eventually must be returned to the woods where they adjust themselves to the new environment with difficulty. Hand-raised deer seldom become wild, and tame bucks are dangerous during the mating season. The chances of survival for tame deer returned to the forest are small.

Frank Dufresne photo   Courtesy Fish and Wildlife Service

Fig. 2.—Spotted fawn of White-tailed Deer.

The antlers which make deer heads such good trophies are peculiar to the deer family alone and should not be confused with the horns of other mammals. Antlers are made of solid bone and are shed once each year by a clean break near the skull, while horns have only a bony core surrounded by a horny sheath and are a permanent fixture, never shed (except in the case of the pronghorned antelope). Early in the spring the budding antlers appear as soft knobs on the deer's forehead, and until fall remain fleshy and filled with blood vessels. During this time when they are in the "velvet" they are easily injured by striking some object. After the velvet has been rubbed from the hardened antlers in early fall, the buck is in a fighting mood and often clashes with other bucks for possession of does or mastery of the forest. Sometimes these clashes end in disaster for both contestants when their antlers become locked together, and unable to free themselves, both die of starvation. After the mating season is over, the antlers are dropped and the warlike bucks are meek and inoffensive again until fall.

Among all the mammals of Virginia certainly none is more majestic than the **wapiti** or **elk,** and it is often referred to even as the king of all deer. In stature it is as large as our domestic cattle, and its antlers, which as in the white-tailed deer are borne only by the bull or stag, are sometimes so large and heavy that it would seem that they should make the animal's head droop. Yet there is no other animal which holds its head so high and arrogantly as the elk.

Actually, the name elk is a misnomer when applied to our native animal, for the name originated in Europe where it applies to an animal similar to the moose of northern North America, and which has not the slightest resemblance to the animal we call elk. The Indian name, wapiti, would be a much better and more appropriate name for us to use. In most respects our elk is similar to its smaller relative, the white-tailed deer, though it is more of a wanderer. Elk from the Giles-Bland Range have appeared in all sections of southwest Virginia and one tagged individual even strayed 250 miles to Snow Hill in eastern North Carolina! In cultivated sections they jump fences with the same ease that we would step over a curbstone. They are not frightened by dogs and actually cower their would-be tormentors, and it is said that on the western ranges a few elk with each flock of sheep are sufficient to protect the animals from the attacks of dogs and wolves!

The elk is not nearly as prolific as the deer, for while the deer may bear twins yearly, elk as a rule bear only one offspring annually.

The head and antlers of the elk make such a prize trophy that hundreds of hunters are attracted each year to Virginia's elk range to try their luck. For this sport they are indebted to the State Game Commission for its restocking program, for elk were completely exterminated in all the eastern states in the latter part of the nineteenth century by the march of civilization. Early explorers and settlers found elk abundant everywhere they traveled in Virginia, from the seacoast to the highest mountains. Seton (1929) quoted Purchas as saying that Captain George Weymouth, during his voyage to Virginia in 1605, found "Deer, red and fallow, Bears, etc.....Some like our other beasts, the savages sign unto us with hornes and broad ears, which we take to be olks or Loshes." Clayton (1694) writing of "beasts" in Virginia said: "there are abundance of brave red deer so that a good woodsman, as they call them, will keep a house in venison." Beverly (1722), Alvord and Bidgood (1912), and others, in accounts of the first expeditions into the western mountains of Virginia spoke of the elk as being plentiful on the broad level plains, and John Clayton who lived in

F. M. Dille photo   Courtesy Fish and Wildlife Service

Fig. 3.—Wapiti.

Gloucester County, writing to a friend in London in 1739, mentioned the occurrence of elk in the State [*Virginia Historical Magazine,* 7(2):172-174]. In 1781, Thomas Jefferson wrote: "I can say with best information that in Virginia the elk has abounded much, and [still] exists in smaller numbers."

Elk were restocked in Virginia from Yellowstone National Park in 1917 and again in 1935. By 1940 it was estimated that Virginia's two elk herds probably numbered about 125 individuals, of which 100 were in the Giles-Bland Range and 25 were in the Botetourt-Bedford Range. The yearly kill of bulls and illegally killed cows during the annual three-day open season averaged about 10 individuals. As most hunting was done in the Giles-Bland Range this represented a 10% yearly kill and kept the size of the herd in a fairly static condition. Unfortunately for the elk, they have a fondness for the corn which is left shocked through the winter in the high mountain fields. Fences can't keep them out and scarecrow devices don't frighten them for long, so each year the State is called upon to pay the farmers for damages to the corn which the elk consume and ruin. To reduce the damages the elk herd was itself reduced. The four-day open season in 1944 made every elk a legal elk, and over sixty were killed, including cows and eight-month-old calves. No recent estimate of the size of the herd left has been made. Virginia, since 1925, has had the distinction of being the only eastern state in which the elk was a game animal, but only wise conservation measures and solution of the elk-farmer relationship problem can preserve elk hunting as a sport in Virginia for the future.

The third and last, but by no means the least of our big game mammals is the **black bear**. Like the elk, it once enjoyed state-wide distribution, but is now confined to a fraction of its former range, occurring only in the great Dismal Swamp and the more rugged sections of the mountains.

Captain John Smith found the bear common in eastern Virginia between the years 1606 and 1612 (Arber 1910). Abraham Wood's expedition, the first to traverse the State from east to west (1671), killed and observed many bear along their route (Alvord and Bidgood 1912). Clayton (1694) wrote that "Bears there are and yet but few in the inhabited part of Virginia; toward Carolina there are many more. There was a small bear killed within three miles of James City the year that I left the country." In the Blue Ridge Mountains bear were killed almost daily, often three per day, by the Spottswood Expedition, 1716 (Thornton, 1896). Boyd (1929) writing of the Virginia-North Carolina dividing line histories, quoted from William Byrd's diary (1728): "We had the fortune to kill a brace of Bucks, as many Bears, and one wild Turkey. The Bears were left with the turkey Buzzards and the venison was taken along." In 1854 Audubon and Bachman wrote of their experiences with bears in the mountains of Virginia. Concerning

Leo K. Couch photo Courtesy Fish and Wildlife Service

Fig. 4—Black Bear cub at Big Levels Wildlife Refuge, George Washington National Forest, Virginia.

the abundance of the bear in the Dismal Swamp, A. K. Fisher wrote in his journal that it was "Very common—in the fall of 1893 George Nichols shot 13. He usually paddled along the lake shore and shot them from sweet gum trees, the berries of which they are very fond of." Wayland (1912) reported that W. B. Ninnick of

E. P. Griffith photo   Courtesy Peninsula Sportsmen's Assoc.

Fig. 5.—Specimens of the Black Bear killed in Virginia and exhibited by the Peninsula Sportsmen's Association.

The bear in the upper center of the photo was killed by W. N. Haldeman of Hampton, Virginia, in the Dismal Swamp in November, 1944. It appears to be one of the largest ever recorded for eastern North America. See page 127.

Broadway, Rockingham County, killed 13 bear in his home county during the season of 1890.

Nowhere in Virginia today are bears as abundant as the old-timers found them, and fortunately too, for renegade bears cause such fearful losses among sheep in high mountain meadows that to many mountain stockmen they are the most hated of all our mammals. Once a bear has enjoyed a dinner of mutton it will sometimes return again and again to the same flock of sheep, and usually will carry or drag its victim several miles before settling down to the meal. The accepted procedure for dealing with such a problem is to hunt down and kill the marauder, using hounds to track it down. It should be realized, though, that every bear is not a bad bear, and one sheep-killer shouldn't condemn the whole tribe. Normally a bear's diet consists mostly of insects and berries and what other animal and vegetable food it can secure. It often digs out chipmunks, and even mice, and frogs and crawfish are frequently enjoyed. During the berry season blackberries, wild cherries, gum berries, and other fruits are all staple foods, and small trees are sometimes stripped of their limbs in the bear's eagerness to get at the juicy fruits. Fresh green corn is a fond delicacy, and in late fall acorns and beechnuts are devoured literally by the bushel. Quantities of ants are eaten by gouging a paw into a nest and then licking off the angry ants when they crawl up onto the paw. The bear's fondness for honey is legendary, and it sometimes goes to great lengths to extract honey from a hive. In more northern regions, quantities of fish are eaten during the spawning season, but not so much in Virginia, where fish runs are not so pronounced.

The colder months of the winter are spent in hibernation, but unlike the groundhog and the jumping mouse, the bear does not go into a complete stupor, and often gets out of its bed of leaves or brush and moves around on the warmer days. Often its tracks may be seen in deep snow, so it is possible that not all individuals partake of the winter sleep. The young, which may number from one to four, are born in early spring just before the mother bear comes out of hibernation. The gestation period is long and litters are produced only every other year. At birth cubs are very tiny, weighing less than a pound, but by summer they have grown large enough to follow their mother all over the forest. At this stage they are cuteness personified and have been rightly called the

clowns of the forest because of their antics in tumbling and clown-
ing and chasing each other up and down trees. But cute as they
may be, they should be left strictly alone, for chances are ten to
one that their mother is nearby, and a mother bear is one of the
most jealous of woodland parents. Bears normally will not attack
humans, and usually go leisurely off in pursuit of their own business
when they encounter men, but a mother bear is an easily enraged
and very dangerous beast. Woe to the person who makes one
angry, for they can climb trees with but little less agility than a
cat and on level ground have been clocked at a speed of 30 miles
per hour!

Even a full-grown six-hundred-pound bear is a playful creature,
and no zoo or side show would be without one. In the woods
they seem to get considerable pleasure from destroying woodland
trail signs, and a particularly jovial individual may tear down signs
as often as they are replaced. Examination of torn or shattered
Forest Service signs in our National Forests will usually reveal
the imprint of a bear's sharp claws, showing how the damage was
done by one swat from a mighty forepaw.

In former times more than now the bear was one of the most
important mammals of the forest. Its hide and fur made a warm
robe, its meat was a staple food, and its fat was burned as tallow.
As a matter of fact, all of the big game mammals were of para-
mount importance to the pioneers. Deer, elk, bear, and buffalo
meat were the main items of subsistence, and their hides, especially
of the deer, were much used for clothing. It is doubtful whether
our country could have developed so rapidly had it not been for
these animals.

Whereas the fame and importance of the large game mammals
rest in their size and in the magnificence of their heads as trophies,
the importance of the smaller game mammals rests in their abundance. Probably any one of the small game mammals is more
numerous than all the big game mammals put together. Virginia
is blessed with a wide variety of this small game, of which perhaps
the most important is the common **cottontail rabbit.** Certainly
the friendly cottontail needs little description, since it is probably
the most familiar of all Virginia's game animals. Occurring in
practically every part of every county in the State, it is known to
farmer and townsman alike. Who hasn't driven along a country

road in the early morning hours and flushed a cottontail at almost
every turn, or who hasn't seen one in his garden, or his woodlot
or pasture?

Along with squirrels, more rabbits fall prey each year to boys'
rifles and sportsmen's guns than all other Virginia game animals
put together. They are at once the first target and proving ground
for boys who will someday be fox hunters, or deer hunters, or
soldiers. Yet with all its popularity as a game animal, the cottontail flourishes year after year in undiminished numbers.

The cottontail is also important as food for many of our predatory
birds and mammals. Indeed, it forms the bulk of the diet of the
fox and the great horned owl, and is eaten in lesser numbers by
hawks, bears, weasels, and bobcats. Where rabbits are abundant,
these predators are much less likely to prey on quail and other birds,
and their raids on poultry yards are noticeably less frequent.

Its rapid rate of reproduction more than any other factor pro-
tects the rabbit from the continual onslaughts of man and beast.
In a shallow fur-lined nest fashioned by the mother rabbit are
born tiny, red, almost hairless, sightless creatures which in a few
days leave the nest as baby cottontails. One rabbit may produce
two or even three litters of from 3 to 7 young in the course of a
year, often bearing the first before all the snows have gone, and
the last after the first fall frosts. As the mother rabbit carefully
covers the nest over with fur and trash each time she leaves it, it
is not often discovered even though it may be placed in such conspicuous places as the lawn or flower bed.

Though the cottontail may become a serious nuisance around
gardens and orchards, through its fondness for the bark of young
trees and for the leaves of some vegetables, it may be easily controlled by trapping and transplanting to some other neighborhood
where it is less likely to offend.

Unfortunately, rabbit hunting has lately been discouraged by
the occurrence of the disease "tularemia," which is sometimes fatal
to man. Caused by a tiny bacterium, the disease is transmitted
to the blood of the rabbit by the tick. Hunters need not be alarmed
by the fear of tularemia if a few simple rules are observed:

1. Don't handle a rabbit (or squirrel) which appears to be sluggish or
   sick, for it may have tularemia.

2. Don't hunt rabbits until cold weather has set in. The infection-carrying tick drops off the rabbit and dies with the advent of cold weather, and by the time the hunting season opens in November, most diseased rabbits have died, leaving only a healthy, disease-free stock.

3. For absolute protection use rubber gloves when dressing a rabbit. The disease is carried in the animal's blood, and once the meat is cooked there is no danger. There is no reason to forego the pleasures of rabbit-stew just because a few rabbits may have tularemia.

O. J. Murie photo   Courtesy Fish and Wildlife Service

Fig. 6.—Varying Hare

Rabbits are gnawing mammals, similar in structure and habits to the rodents, but are placed in a separate order, Lagomorpha, because they have four incisors or gnawing teeth in the upper jaw instead of two as the rodents have.

Several kinds of rabbits are known to inhabit Virginia, but only the common cottontail has state-wide distribution. In the Dismal Swamp and other nearby lowlands, the water-loving, dark-tailed **marsh rabbit** is locally common, and at elevations above 3,000 feet in the mountains the little short-eared **New England cottontail** is the common rabbit. In a few wild areas in the mountains the large **varying hare** occurs. Its tracks in the snow are twice as large as those of the cottontail, giving rise to the name snowshoe rabbit. In summer it has a reddish-brown coat similar to the cottontail, but as winter approaches the brown hairs are shed to give way to a white coat which makes it almost invisible in snowy landscapes.

It is locally known as "white rabbit" and the cottontail as "gray rabbit." Due to its size and wariness, the hare would make an excellent game animal if it were reintroduced into some of our higher mountain areas where its principal food plants, spruce and fir, occur.

Several members of the Order Rodentia, or gnawers, are represented on our list of game animals, and though the most numerous of the rodents are mice and rats, the most conspicuous are squirrels, which are among the most important of our game animals.

The gray squirrel is the commonest of our game squirrels, often occurring in such numbers as to become a distinct nuisance. It is at home wherever oaks or other nut trees occur, whether it be on the highest mountain or in a coastal swamp. In parks and towns the gray squirrel becomes tame and friendly, and is often seen in such unsquirrel-like places as on telephone cables and clothes-line poles, or eating corn with the chickens in the poultry yard. It will travel considerable distances across open land to feast on green or shocked corn and may cause considerable damage when numerous.

In the forests, however, the gray squirrel is quite a different animal, ever shy and wary, and unless it is betrayed by the splatter of hickory-nut shells below the tree in which it is feeding, it may go unseen, for its angry scolding is heard much less frequently here than in more civilized places.

Hunters prefer a September open season on squirrels, because at this season when the squirrels are busy cutting hickory nuts, it takes much less vigilance to hunt them. At this season many helpless youngsters perish in their nests when their mothers are killed. September hunting is not only cruel but wasteful, because for every mother squirrel which does not return to her young, there are from two to three less squirrels to hunt later in the season.

Unlike rabbits, squirrels cannot be eradicated from a neighborhood by moving them to another area unless it is several miles distant, for they have a strong homing instinct and will travel as much as three miles or more across open country to return to a favorite home spot. For a nest they prefer a hole in a tree, or will settle for a bird nest box, but many, especially in the summer, construct cozy ball-shaped leaf nests which are quite waterproof and comfortable, even though they may be located in the wind-swept outer branches of a tree.

Squirrels are frequently caught by weasels and foxes or other predatory animals when they are surprised on the ground, often

Courtesy Fish and Wildlife Service

Fig. 7.—Fox Squirrel.

W. B. Bell photo

while digging for nuts which they buried for winter use. Their most feared enemies, though, excepting man, are red-tailed and red-shouldered hawks. When pressed, a squirrel will jump without hesitation even from the highest oak, using its bushy tail as a parachute, and landing with a thud, apparently unhurt.

Considerably larger and more robust, our other game squirrel, the **fox squirrel,** occurs in many sections of the State, but most commonly in the mountains. It is more frequently found in orchards and in isolated groves than is the smaller gray squirrel and spends relatively more of its time on the ground, but has equal sporting qualities. In the lowlands it seems to prefer the heavy gum and pine timber. On the Eastern Shore, where a bluish-gray subspecies occurs, the fox squirrel is called "gray squirrel" and the gray squirrel, "cat squirrel." What could be more confusing?

Very unsquirrel-like, both in appearance and in habits, the **woodchuck,** or groundhog, is nevertheless placed in the squirrel family on the basis of its internal structure. Though it may climb into the lower branches of trees, it spends the greater part of its life in its underground burrow, where it is secure from most of its enemies except the weasel. Skunks, 'possums, rabbits and foxes also frequently use its burrows either as a permanent home or as a temporary retreat.

In some sections the woodchuck lives in fields and meadows or near gardens, where it eats great quantities of grass, alfalfa, or vegetable leaves and literally becomes a ground "hog." These animals of the fields lay on thick layers of fat and soon after the first frost retreat to their burrows where they remain dormant (in "hibernation") until the first warm days of spring. They usually sleep right through "Groundhog Day," February the second.

The woodchuck that lives along the river bluffs, in the forests, and in cliffs and rockslides is the same animal as the chuck of the fields, but lives up to the name "woodchuck" and isn't a "hog" at all. On the contrary, it is generally sleek and thin and its winter sleep is not nearly as long as that of its country cousin. The leaves, bark, berries and nuts that it finds in its forest haunts are hardly as fattening as the tender grass and alfalfa of the fields.

Hunting the chuck with a rifle is a common sport, and the meat of the woodland animal makes a very edible dish, while the meat

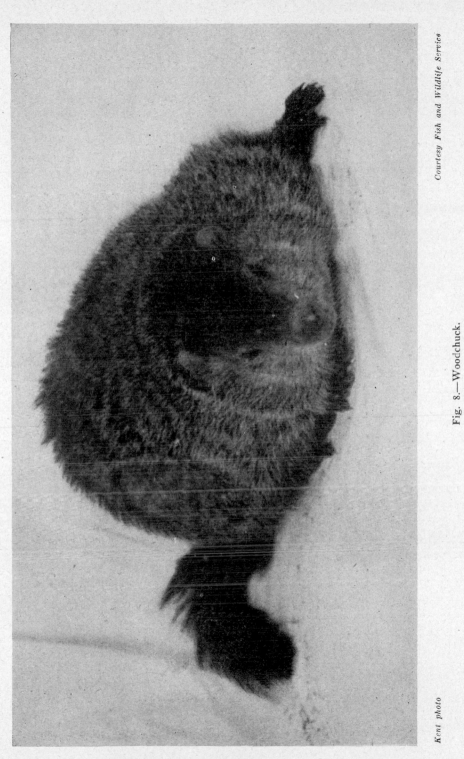

Fig. 8.—Woodchuck.

of the meadow animal often is too fat and greasy to be enjoyed. Though its hide is practically worthless, many a young trapper has tested his prowess on the woodchuck, since it is one of the most easily trapped animals of its size, and, indeed, it is as a boy's game animal that the chuck is most important.

Red and **gray foxes** occur commonly throughout the State, though by preference they choose different habitats. The red fox prefers fields and meadows and woods borders and seems to survive just as well in areas heavily cultivated as in wilder regions where the gray fox is at home.

Both species are widely hunted, the red fox especially in northern Virginia and the gray more in the mountain sections, and neither seems to suffer particularly, no matter how heavy the hunting may be. As a matter of fact, the fox may even enjoy the hunt if the terrain is in its favor, and more often than not its reputation for slyness—"sly as a fox"—pays off when, after a merry chase before the baying and panting hounds, it loses itself in the mountain fastness or brush.

The red fox's burrow or den is often located under a bush or thicket in an open field or under a log or tree in open woods, and frequently the fox may be seen sprawled before the den enjoying the morning sun. Usually when it is disturbed in this pleasant pastime it bounds away rather than scurrying into the den, apparently hoping that by this maneuver its home will go unnoticed. On the other hand, the gray fox chooses a crevice in a cliff or rock slide, or a burrow beneath a tree or stump, and being much shyer than the red fox, is seldom seen.

As proved by stomach analyses, rabbits and meadow mice form the bulk of the fox's diet, along with berries, nuts and corn in the summer and fall. Yellow-jacket nests dug out by foxes are a common sight. When mice and rabbits are scarce, then the foxes are more likely to turn to poultry and game birds for their livelihood, and some individuals may become quite destructive. But where foxes and other flesh-eating animals and birds have been completely wiped out by trapping and shooting, mice multiply to the point where they destroy crops and vegetation and game birds become scarce for lack of food. Thus, while the fox itself may be destructive, its presence is needed to maintain a natural balance.

In the North the red fox occurs in several color phases, one of which is the much sought silver fox, but here in Virginia along the southern fringe of the red fox's range, the occurrence of the silver phase is extremely rare. However, hundreds of silver foxes are raised annually on fur farms in our mountains. Due to the large number shot or trapped each year, the red fox is one of Virginia's more important fur animals, each skin bringing several dollars. Because of the coarseness of its fur the pelt of the gray fox is of less value.

V. K. Irion photo   Courtesy La. Dept. of Conservation

Fig. 9.—Raccoon.

Although the **raccoon** is best known to "coon" hunters, and is seldom seen by others due to its nocturnal habits, its peculiar masked face and ringed tail are familiar to almost everyone. It belongs to the order Carnivora or flesh-eaters and its nearest relative is the bear. Like the bear, its diet is varied and usually consists of almost anything edible which it may happen upon. In its favorite habitats along streams and in swamps, where it usually builds its den in the hollow of a tree, it delights in hunting crawfish, snails, small fish, aquatic insects and almost anything else that moves. Mice and birds are frequently captured, and disappearance of eggs and baby chicks often follows its visits to barnyards. Quantities of corn, berries and fruit are consumed in season. The widespread belief that the "coon" always washes its food before eating is not always true, since many of its meals are consumed far away from water. Many captive coons fail to show this trait.

E. W. Craven photo   Courtesy Fish and Wildlife Service

Fig. 10.—Opossum with young.

Perhaps the raccoon's main claim to fame lies in the use of its fur for the coonskin cap of the pioneer. Certainly in those days it was of more importance than it is today, because in many sections the coonskin was a medium of exchange. As a game animal it is of most importance today. It is hunted at night, being pursued with hounds until finally treed. Where the sport of the chase ends the profit begins, for even in this age of chinchillas and blue minks its fur still has considerable value.

The **opossum** is another animal much hunted at night with

hounds, especially in the South. In many sections it is an important source of food, but elsewhere it is hunted more for the sport. Usually it is treed after a short chase by the hounds and frequently after it has been captured it feigns death, or "plays 'possum," as the popular saying goes. Its fur is of only small value, but so many pelts are sold each year that it has a rather important standing on our list of furbearers.

It seems quite unafraid of man and often abounds within the limits of large cities, where it subsists on mice, frogs, birds, edible refuse, and almost anything else it may pick up. In its more natural habitat in the country, in thickets, woods, swamps, and orchards, it may add berries, nuts, apples, birds' eggs and young, fish and green corn to its meal, and persimmons are eaten with greed. Its visits to barnyards are frequently destructive.

The opossum is the most primitive mammal occurring in Virginia, or in North America, for that matter. It belongs to the order of pouched mammals called Marsupialia which is most abundant in Australia and which includes such well-known forms as the kangaroo, koala bear, and Tasmanian wolf. Among these mammals the young are born only a few days after conception and in a very early stage of development. In the opossum, for instance, the young are so tiny at birth that the whole litter of 12 to 18 would hardly fill a teaspoon. After birth they make their way into the marsupium or pouch on the mother's belly and there remain until they have grown to the size of mice. Then they begin to move about, and soon afterward are large enough to shift for themselves. The opossum is the only North American mammal which has this marsupial pouch.

Fig. 11.—Muskrat houses on Deadwood Marsh, Blackwater Refuge, Cambridge, Maryland.

FURBEARERS

Second in importance only to the game mammals and actually much more important in dollars and cents are our furbearers. Even though Virginia does not rank high among the fur-producing states because of the lack of extensive forests and marshlands, still thousands each year pick up extra cash amounting to nearly a half million dollars through their trapping activities.

With the most valuable of the furbearers, the beaver, the fisher, and the otter, now completely protected, the **muskrat** is today our most important fur producer. It has a state-wide distribution, but is by far the most numerous in the big coastal marshes, less common along the rivers, and generally uncommon along the mountain and forest streams. In marshes it usually builds its nest in a dome-shaped pile of rushes or reeds constructed in a patch of open water, but along streams, a burrow into the bank usually harbors the nest. There may be one, two or even three litters of from five to ten young each in a year, so it is no wonder that the muskrat remains plentiful even though heavily trapped.

The stems and roots of water and marsh plants and aquatic insects and animals are the muskrat's main foods and only infrequently do its habits interfere with the interests of man. When it burrows into pond banks and causes leakages and unsightly holes where its burrows have caved in, it becomes quite objectionable, but properly constructed dams reduce this damage. As muskrats make frequent excursions, even going considerable distances overland, they soon find newly constructed ponds, and if they are to their liking they immediately take up residence.

The muskrat resembles an overgrown meadow mouse, specialized for an aquatic existence. It is an expert swimmer and diver, using its enlarged, partially webbed hind feet for propulsion and its long laterally flattened tail as a rudder. As the entrances to its burrows are always under water, it is comparatively safe from all its enemies save the mink and otter when it is in its nest, but when feeding it is in eternal danger from other enemies, such as the dog and the fox.

Another rodent of vast importance as a furbearer, the **beaver,** is today on the protected list in most of the eastern United States while it stages a comeback from the virtual extinction suffered

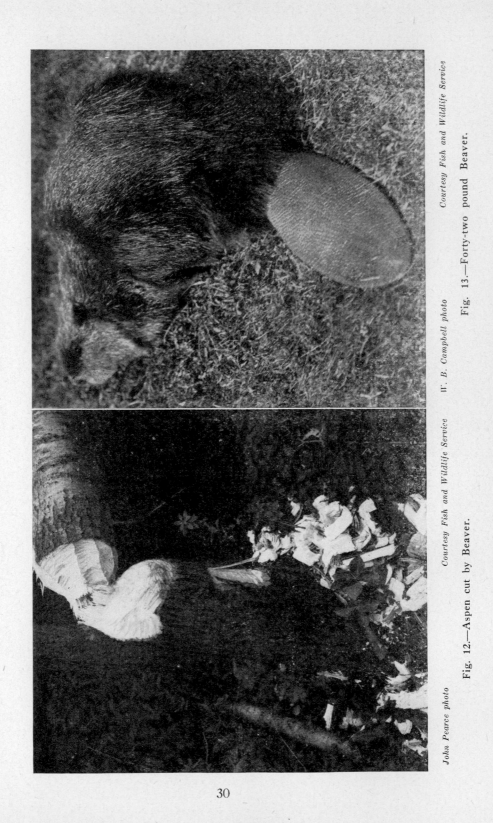

John Pearce photo   Courtesy Fish and Wildlife Service   W. B. Campbell photo   Courtesy Fish and Wildlife Service

Fig. 12.—Aspen cut by Beaver.   Fig. 13.—Forty-two pound Beaver.

during the first two decades of this century. Beaver restocked by the State Game Commission and conservation-minded individuals have now become established in nineteen Virginia counties, but because of its clash with man's interests, it will never regain all of its former range which once encompassed virtually the entire State. Since a colony of beavers may ruin a valuable orchard, wreck a corn crop, or flood rich farmland, considerable care and foresight should be exercised before introductions are made to a stream. A survey to determine which streams of the State are most suitable for beaver would be a valuable aid to future re-stocking programs.

The habits of the beaver are practically legendary, and there are few people who are not familiar with the stories of its dams, canals, lodges, tree cutting, and other engineering feats. The old saying "busy as a beaver" points it up as being one of the most industrious of all mammals. It takes a lot of energy to construct and maintain a dam eight feet high, sixteen feet thick, and a hundred or even a thousand feet long, or to fell a tree six inches to five feet in diameter, but it's all in a day's work for a colony of beavers. However, the story of the beaver using its broad flat tail as a trowel for carrying mud and dam-building materials is just a story. Actually its only uses are as a rudder when swimming, as a prop when cutting a tree, and for slapping the water as an alarm in times of danger.

The beaver's chief food is the bark and twigs of trees, willow, poplar and birch being preferred, and large quantities of sticks and logs are stored on the bottom of the beaver pond for winter use. Besides their use for food storage, the ponds also serve as refuge from the beaver's many enemies. Where it is not molested, the beaver usually constructs large dome-shaped lodges of sticks, in which it places its nest, but sometimes the nest is built in a burrow in the stream bank. Each year a single litter of four to six young is born during April or May.

The beaver is the largest North American rodent and is one of the most valuable furbearers. Its dams on mountain streams con-trol the run-off of rainfall and help prevent floods. From the standpoint of human interest, it is one of the most important mammals. With continued restocking and wise protection, the beaver should once again become a valuable asset to Virginia economy.

Several of the carnivorous or flesh-eating mammals produce valuable pelts and are among our more important furbearers. The black bear furnished warm robes for the Indians and the first settlers; the raccoon gave Daniel Boone and the other pioneer woodsmen their famous coonskin caps, and foxes have furnished furs favored for centuries as neckpieces and garment material. Other carnivores, including the mink, the weasels, the skunks and the bobcats, are of importance. Foremost of these is the **mink,** abundant in its natural habitats often close to the dwellings of man and extensively raised on fur farms. The farm-raised blue and white mutations of the mink are among the most valuable furs in the world.

Like most of its weasel relatives, the mink is noted for its blood-thirsty disposition, and apparently kills at times purely for the love of killing. Anything that moves and is no more than twice its size may become its prey. Mice and rabbits are its most frequent victims, but it often catches birds and snakes and may make occasional raids on poultry houses. It is an excellent swimmer and has no difficulty adding muskrats, frogs, crawfish, salamanders and fish to its fare. It may even attack beaver at times.

While its preferred habitat seems to be stream banks and swamps, the mink may be encountered almost anywhere, even at great distances from water. Frequently it has no permanent den and may wander considerable distances in quest of food, often covering a watershed of several square miles. When permanent dens are established, they are usually located near streams beneath stumps or logs or in rock piles. Four to eight young are born in April or May.

Because of its nocturnal habits, the mink is not usually observed except by trappers, unless it is surprised in the early morning or at dusk as it hunts along a stream bank.

The mink's smaller cousin, the **New York weasel,** is abundant in all parts of Virginia except in some of the southeastern counties, and is even less fearful of man than the mink. It often thrives within the corporate limits of towns and cities, but its usual habitat is farmland or woods and it is not so fond of water as the mink.

In the North weasels turn white in winter like the varying hare, but not so in Virginia. In our latitudes white individuals are rare. Nevertheless, the brown pelts have some market value and many are sold from Virginia each year.

Marauding individuals which devastate poultry flocks have given all weasels a bad name. Actually weasels as a group are beneficial to the farmers, for their main items of food are mice and rats. Also, frogs, insects, snakes, and occasionally birds and rabbits become their prey. In deep snows especially, rabbits often become their main objects of attack.

Many of the carnivores besides skunks have obnoxious odors, and weasels and the mink are not exceptions. The odor given off by an angered or excited weasel can be almost as offensive and nauseating as that of the skunk. Weasels are built like a stick of dynamite—every inch packs power, and they are so strongly muscled that it is no easy matter to kill one by breaking its back or neck.

The weasel's insatiable curiosity often leads to its downfall. Once it has gained the safety of its burrow or den it will almost invariably pop its head out again so as not to miss anything going on outside, or if it is more wary, a simple squeaking noise will bring it bounding again into the open. Sometimes a weasel will carefully explore all about the feet of a person standing perfectly motionless.

Occurring only in the mountainous portion of the State and even there considered rare, the **least weasel** is in many respects only a New York weasel in miniature. Both in habits and general appearance it resembles its larger cousin, but its tail is not black-tipped, and since it is only about half as large, its diet consists of smaller animals such as mice, shrews, and insects. One was caught at Blacksburg, Virginia, on the fifth floor of a building in the Wildlife Office, where it had probably gone in search of mice! The least weasel is so small that it has practically no value as a furbearer.

The **otter** is another furbearer closely related to the weasels. It is considerably larger than the mink and is an accomplished swimmer, able to prey even on the swift and agile trout. Its home is the water, and most of its diet is made up of various types of fish supplemented by frogs, crawfish, mussels, snails and aquatic insects.

In Virginia it is most abundant in the river swamps, but seems to be becoming increasingly common in the mountain rivers and creeks. As it is shy and retiring and mostly nocturnal in habit it is seldom seen except while enjoying its "slide." Apparently for the mere pleasure of it, otters slide down steep banks into the water,

W. H. Burt photo   *Courtesy Univ. Mich. Mus. Zool.*

Fig. 14.—Otter, still dripping from dive.

folding their front feet against their sides and plunging head first into the water. Although otter fur is the most durable American fur and brings a good price, the otter is too rare in Virginia to rank as an important furbearer.

Virginia skunks are of two kinds and both are so well known that they need little description. By far the commonest, and occurring all over the State, the **striped skunk** or pole cat is also the larger of the two kinds. The smaller **spotted skunk** or civet cat occurs only in the mountainous portion of the State.

Without a doubt, the skunk's greatest claim to fame lies in the obnoxious odor of the fluid secreted by two glands near the base of the tail. This familiar odor may carry as much as a mile if the weather conditions are right, and it is so penetrating that clothing impregnated with it bears a trace of the smell for a very long time. Exposure to air and sunlight are the best methods of removing the odor. The fluid, which may be thrown in jets as far as 10 or 15 feet, has an intensely acid reaction and will bleach clothing with remarkable efficiency.   It is said that the only safe way to pick up a skunk is by the tail, but this is not 100 percent effective.

The skunk is a slow lumbering beast practically without defense except for its odor, but this is a fairly potent weapon except against horned owls, and occasionally against red-tailed hawks and foxes. These three are sometimes quite willing to sacrifice personal vanity for a good meal.   The skunk may frequently be seen abroad on

Clyde P. Patton photo

Fig. 15.—Striped skunk

cloudy days or toward dusk, although it is primarily nocturnal. At such times it immediately raises its tail in warning to the intruder and waddles off on its way.

For living quarters, it may make a burrow of its own or com-
mandeer a rabbit or woodchuck burrow, or build a nest under a
building. Much to the sorrow of the residents, it frequently nests
under porches in towns. Its young number from four to eight and
are born in late spring. In Virginia the striped skunk is found
more around farms and other open lands than in forests, while the
little spotted skunk is commonest in rocky, broken, wooded regions.

Skunks are generally beneficial in their food habits and only
infrequently steal eggs or baby chickens. They eat many insects,
and their little cone-shaped grubbings where beetles and worms
were sought are a common sight in fields. Mice, snakes, grass-
hoppers and crickets are staple foods and many nests of turtle
eggs are dug up and eaten. Sometimes bird nests are destroyed and
quantities of berries and wild fruits are consumed in season.

The fur of both species of skunks is much in demand but black
pelts of the striped skunk are the more valuable. The value of
the pelt decreases according to the amount of white it contains.

Of minor importance as a furbearer and game animal, but often
relatively important because of undesirable habits, the **bobcat** occurs
throughout the wilder portions of the State. It is most abundant
in broken and rocky forest or brushlands and in swamps, where it
dens in a crevice or a burrow. Its litter of two to four young is
born in the spring. As it has shy and retiring habits, the bobcat
is seldom seen except when treed by a fox hunter's hounds, or when
glimpsed as it crosses the road ahead of a car. In some districts
its eerie night screams are frequently heard, but generally it is
silent as a shadow.

It is a powerful animal, powerful enough even to slay a deer under
some circumstances, but smaller animals and birds are its main
items of food. Rabbits, mice and squirrels are its usual fare, and it
may occasionally attack foxes, muskrats and minks when the opportunity presents itself. Some grouse and small birds are eaten
and it does not disdain beetles and other insects. On outlying
farms it picks off stray chickens and turkeys and sometimes small
pigs and lambs, but it is not usually a problem when stock is properly penned. As far as predatory cats are concerned, the wild
or semi-wild house cat is a more serious problem than the bobcat.
The house cat is a confirmed killer of birds and because of its

greater numbers is many times more destructive than the bobcat. The house cat also eats mice, but not in sufficient quantities to offset the damage it does to beneficial birds.

Two other animals, the opossum and the rabbit, are of lesser importance as furbearers, and have already been discussed in the

B. S. Wilkins photo   Courtesy Fish and Wildlife Service

Fig. 16.—Young Bobcat.

chapter on game animals. The only other Virginia mammal which might be properly mentioned in this chapter is the mole. In Europe the mole is widely trapped for its soft thick fur. The common mole of eastern North America has fur of similar quality, but almost all of our commercial mole fur is imported from Europe.

RODENTS

Mammals like deer, bear, rabbits, and foxes are conspicuous and familiar to everyone and are of recognized importance since they can easily be given a cash value, but we often lose sight of the myriads of small mammals which vastly outnumber their larger brothers both in number of individuals and in number of species and are also of immense economic importance. Unfortunately, the degree of importance can not be readily assessed in terms of dollars and cents. It will not be denied, however, that the rats that destroy a shock of corn, or that the mice that fatten in a granary, have much economic importance. Nor is the mouse without importance that unwillingly gives itself up as food to a hungry hawk or fox which might otherwise have eaten a game bird or animal. The mouse that girdles a valuable apple tree is of economic importance also.

The small mammals occurring in Virginia fall into two great groups, the rodents and the insectivores. The rodents are a great and very diversified order of mammals which are represented in Virginia by no less than 25 species. Nearly one-third of all the species of mammals recorded for the State are rodents. They are all characterized by large chisel-like front teeth especially adapted to gnawing and are thus an order of gnawers. Rodents are just as much at home in the salt marshes and on the beaches along the coast as in the cloud-drenched spruce forests of our highest mountains, and as a result of their widely varying habitats they have developed numerous and very dissimilar forms, adapted to arboreal, terrestrial, subterranean, and aquatic life. Even though they may outwardly seem unrelated, groundhogs, squirrels, beavers, mice, rats, and porcupines are all rodents and all closely related.

We have already considered some of the larger and more conspicuous rodents, including the game squirrels, the beavers, and the muskrat, in previous chapters. Besides the large game species, several other squirrels occur in Virginia. These include the chipmunk, red squirrel, and flying squirrel. The **chipmunk** is one of the smallest of our squirrels and unlike its larger relatives spends most of its time on the ground and usually builds its nest in a subterranean burrow. Hence the common name, ground squirrel. Except for the colder days of winter, which it spends in hibernation, the chipmunk is abroad the year around, and its cheery chirping and clucking are well-known woodland sounds. The chipmunk is not confined to the forest, however, and is often common in road banks, along fence rows, in barnyards, and sometimes even in city

W. H. Burt photo   Courtesy Univ. Mich. Mus. Zool.
Fig. 17.—Chipmunk.

parks and yards. Its food consists mostly of seed and grains, nuts, fruits, insects, and an occasional young bird, and it stores large quantities for winter use. Where it invades grain bins and outbuildings it becomes a nuisance, and where it is abundant it is often destructive to shocked corn and wheat, but otherwise it is of little economic importance.

W. H. Burt photo   Courtesy Univ. Mich. Mus. Zool.
Fig. 18.—Red Squirrel, adult and young.

The **red squirrel,** also, spends much more of its time on the ground than do its larger relatives, but it is by no means as terrestrial as the chipmunk. Locally common all over the State, it seems to be completely lacking over wide areas, and is generally

Fig. 19.—Gray Squirrel.

most common in areas of pine, spruce, hemlock and other ever-greens. Its wide distribution has given it a variety of common names, and depending upon the locality it is variously known as pine squirrel, fairy-diddle, mountain boomer, chickaree, and red squirrel. It is so noisy and mischievous that it is the most con-spicuous of all our squirrels, and its presence in a locality seldom goes unnoticed.

The red squirrel is generally active the year around, becoming a "shut-in" only during the coldest weather. Its nest is usually in an old woodpecker hole or in a hollow limb, and during the summer it may construct a ball-shaped leaf nest in the branches of a favorite tree. Like most of the other squirrels its young number from three to six per litter.

It enjoys a wide variety of foods and is perhaps the most omnivorous of our squirrels. The ground under its favorite beech or pine trees is littered by a rain of chips and scales from the seeds and cones it opens, and in the late summer and fall waste chunks of mushrooms and hickory nuts add further variety. It is not very particular, however, and almost any sort of seed or nut or berry is looked upon with favor and insects of various kinds are frequently eaten. Much of its time is spent burying or caching food for winter, and more often than not it lays up much more than it can consume. In this way, the buried acorns and seeds help regenerate the forest. Unfortunately, it does not hesitate to become a nest robber, and its piracy of eggs and baby birds has put it on many a bird-lover's black-list. In most instances, though, it is not a serious menace to bird populations. It is hunted as a game animal in some sections, but because of its small size it is generally passed by.

The last and least of our squirrels is the little **southern flying squirrel,** one of the most charming creatures of the forest. Among all rodents, it alone has partially conquered the air. It does not actually fly, but by extending the membranes along its sides, it is able to glide from tree to tree, often for distances of 100 to 150 feet. Its distribution is state-wide and in some localities it outnumbers all other squirrels, but because of its nocturnal habits it is seldom seen. It is the only one of our squirrels that is active at night and sleeps through the day, and its great black eyes are an expression of this habit.

Its home is usually an old woodpecker hole, but its nest of twigs may be built on an old crow nest, or in a bird box, or even in an attic or outbuilding. During severe cold snaps several may band together in a single nest for added warmth, but under ordinary conditions its soft thick fur allows it to disregard cold and remain active throughout the winter.

The presence of flying squirrels is often revealed by their bird-like chirping in the night, but anyone not familiar with this chirping may go a long time without seeing one. Often whole families are found when old snags are cut in woodlots, and house cats often bring in flying squirrels after their nightly forays. The sounds of flying squirrels' escapades in the attic or in the walls are often mistakenly attributed to rats and may become objectionable. Otherwise, though, it is a harmless animal since it lives mostly on

Courtesy Fish and Wildlife Service

Fig. 20.—Southern Flying Squirrel.

nuts, seeds, fruits and insects. It may occasionally rob bird nests, but not as a regular practice.

Because of its gentle disposition and alert manner, the flying squirrel makes one of the most lovable and interesting of forest pets.

The **northern flying squirrel,** a species considerably larger and darker than the southern flying squirrel, has been found in the spruce and fir forests of West Virginia, Tennessee and North Carolina, and it may yet be found in some of our few remaining areas of spruce and fir. In appearance and habits it resembles the southern flying squirrel, but is perhaps more fond of meat and certainly is more particular about its choice of habitat.

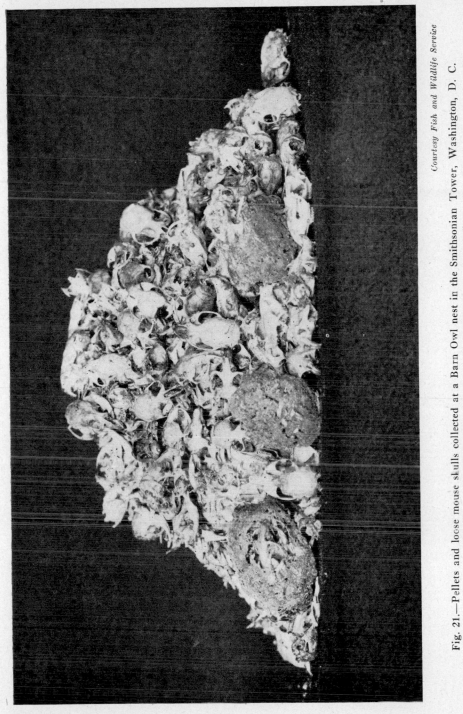

Fig. 21.—Pellets and loose mouse skulls collected at a Barn Owl nest in the Smithsonian Tower, Washington, D. C.

The Barn Owl is a most effective "mouse trap."

Mice and rats make up the largest percentage of Virginia rodents. All of our native mice fall into four general groups, of which the most important economically are the voles. Voles may be roughly described as mice with tails shorter than the head and body. Not all mice with the tail shorter than the head and body are voles, but all short-tailed Virginia mice are. Voles of one kind or another are found in every habitat; field, orchard, marsh, and forest.

Probably the most familiar to a majority of people is the **meadow mouse,** or field mouse as it is often called. It is the mouse that is usually found under shocks of wheat and corn (along with house mice and rats, of course) and is the one most frequently unearthed by the plow and by the family dog. It lives in wet and dry meadows, cultivated fields, marshes, and orchards, but is seldom found in woods. Its nest is a round ball of dried grasses a few inches in diameter which is more often above ground than below.

Among all the mammals of the world, the lowly meadow mouse is one of the most prolific. Its young may number from two to ten per litter, and one mouse may average more than a litter per month! A meadow mouse sometimes bears her first offspring before she is two months old, and in our climate, usually breeds the year around.

With such a high birth rate it may seem strange that this doesn't become a land of meadow mice. The secret lies with the carnivores, for the meadow mouse is the most important single item of food for most of the flesh eaters—hawks, owls, weasels, foxes, and cats. It is consumed by the thousands and millions by these animals. A single barn owl, for instance, may eat four or five or more meadow mice per night every night in the year! The meadow mouse is, then, important economically as food for these flesh-eating birds and mammals.

The meadow mouse is a cyclic mammal, building its population to a peak of abundance and then abruptly declining as a result of disease. This cycle is repeated usually every four years. It is when the meadow mouse is at the bottom of its cycle that the flesh eaters are forced to prey most heavily upon birds, game, and poultry if they are to survive.

The meadow mouse is first of all a vegetarian, but it will eat

almost anything edible that it happens to come across. Tender
leaves and buds, the rootstocks of grass and herbs, bark of trees,
weed seeds, and berries are all favorites. The network of well-
beaten trails, an inch or an inch and a half wide, which are so
common in grasslands usually belong to meadow mice, as do the
little criss-cross piles of grass cut into match lengths. These little
piles are formed in the mouse's effort to reach the seed heads atop
the grass stems.

When snow covers the ground and its usual food supply is cut
off, the meadow mouse sometimes does serious damage by girdling
valuable nursery and orchard stock. In this respect, however, the
pine mouse is a more important offender. The pine mouse is nearly
as large as the meadow mouse but has a very short tail and extremely soft, thick, shiny fur. In this latter respect it resembles the
mole, with which it also shares a subterranean existence. It constructs a remarkable network of tunnels from which it barks the
roots of trees and eats the rootstocks of grasses and herbs. Like the
meadow mouse, and indeed, like all the voles, it is a cyclic species,
and in periods of abundance becomes a serious menace to orchards
and nurseries where it kills the trees by girdling the roots. It is
usually controlled by poisoning or gassing, and hogs also give some
measure of protection by rooting out its burrows.

The pine mouse is by no means restricted to orchards and
nurseries, but is also found in fields and in open woods. Most
of the damage to seeds and roots in gardens and flower beds
which is charged to moles is in actuality the work of pine mice.

The other voles of Virginia are of lesser importance because
their habits do not usually conflict with the interests of man. The
lemming mouse is a stubby-tailed mouse the size of a meadow
mouse which usually prefers boggy or marshy lands for its home,
but it may also be found in brushy openings on mountain slopes.
It occurs throughout western Virginia and in the Dismal Swamp,
but seems to be missing from the intervening region. It is even
more cyclic than the meadow mouse. One year it may be the
commonest mouse in a region and six months later be almost completely absent.

The common woodland vole, the **red-backed mouse,** occurs only
in western Virginia, usually on the cooler, higher slopes, though

it has been found at elevations as low as Big Stone Gap. It feeds largely on the buds and shoots of forest plants, on fruits, nuts, and insects, and is extremely fond of blackberries. It is the most brightly colored of our voles, having a grayish belly, brownish sides, and a broad red stripe down the length of the back.

A fifth species of vole, the **rock vole,** is to be expected in our higher mountains, although it has not been found to date. It is known from West Virginia, North Carolina, and Tennessee, where it occurs in damp forests of spruce and birch among rotted logs and mossy rocks. It is similar in appearance to the meadow mouse but is more orange about the face and flanks. As the meadow

D. A. Spencer photo   Courtesy Fish and Wildlife Service

Fig. 22.—White-footed Mice.

mouse does not usually occur in forest lands except in the openings, any vole caught in the woods and resembling a meadow mouse should be carefully preserved since it might be the rare rock vole.

The second group of native mice, and the commonest woodland mice, is the group of long-tailed species known as white-footed or deer mice. Of these the **white-footed mouse** is the most common and occurs from one end of Virginia to the other in woods, in brushy fields, in thickets, and even in houses. It is probably even better known than the common meadow mouse. The adult is chestnut brown on the back and the young is gray, while both have white bellies and feet. Their most noticeable features, however, are their great black eyes, long whiskers, and large ears.

Unlike the voles, which move about both day and night, the white-footed mouse is nocturnal and is seldom seen abroad during the sunny hours. Again unlike the vole, it does not make well-defined trails. Its nest is a loosely globular affair often a foot in diameter made of shredded bark, hairs, thistle down, wool, or any other readily obtainable material. It is placed in a hollow log, under a stump, in a bird box, or almost anywhere in a house. Young number from two to eight per litter and litters are not so frequent as among the voles. Deer mice are just as numerous as voles, though, for their habitat offers them more protection from their many enemies, yet they are one of the principal foods of the rattle snake and are eaten by animals even as large as the black bear.

In remote areas which have not been invaded by the house mouse, the white-foot makes just as much a nuisance of itself as the more detestable animal when it takes up its abode in dwellings and outhouses.

The white-footed mouse is largely omnivorous in diet, but seems to prefer seeds, nuts, fruits, berries, and insects. It has the interesting habit of storing large quantities of seeds and nuts, often accumulating an amazingly large quantity in a short period of time. Sometimes it will drop its hoard down the spout of a tea kettle or into a milk bottle, with apparently no thought of how it will retrieve its stores. In a house infested with white-footed mice hardly anything is safe from its busy teeth. Soap is eagerly gnawed on, hair brushes are shorn of their bristles, labels of tin cans are shredded, and mattresses are explored.

Two other species of mice so closely resemble the white-footed mouse that it is hard for the average person to distinguish them. On the higher mountain slopes where the soil remains cool and damp the year around, and where the spruce and the birch are the predominant trees, the **deer mouse** is often the most abundant mouse. This friendly little mouse may be found as a frequent table guest at picnics under the spruces on Whitetop during summer evenings. Its longer tail will sometimes serve to distinguish it from the common white-foot of lower elevations.

The **cotton mouse** of the swamps of the southeastern counties is larger than the common white-foot, but resembles it both in habits and in general appearance.

The fourth and last, and most distinctive member of this group is the beautiful **golden mouse.** The bright orange coloration of its upper parts, the cream color of its belly, and its large dark eyes make it the most attractive of our mice. It is rare in the mountains, but elsewhere, wherever there are honeysuckle thickets, it is a common species. Its nest of leaves, bark shreds, or grasses is usually suspended in a honeysuckle vine, one to fifteen feet above the ground, and a shake of the vine will generally bring the occupants scurrying from the nest. The number of young per litter is not usually more than four, and the number of litters per year is probably not more than four to six. In diet and many other habits it is similar to the white-footed mice, but it is not known to invade houses. It is of gentle disposition and makes an interesting pet.

A small group of native mice somewhat uncommon in Virginia and of little economic significance is composed of the **harvest mice.** They are our smallest mice and bear a slight resemblance to the house mouse, from which they may be distinguished with certainty, however, by a conspicuous longitudinal groove on each of the upper incisors, or gnawing teeth. They are at home in meadowland and in alfalfa and timothy fields, usually picking the intermediate zone between the dryer and wetter portions of the field. Their nests are nothing more than small editions of meadow mouse nests and are generally constructed above ground. They thrive on a diet of seeds, grass leaves, and insects, and as far as is known do nothing which might be considered inimical to man.

The jumping mice, the final group of native mice to be considered, are without a doubt the most interesting mice which occur in Virginia, both because of their habits and because of their appearance. Their tails are exceedingly long, almost two-thirds of the total length, their front legs are small, and their hind legs are disproportionately long and kangaroo-like. They are closely kin to the Old World jerboas but only distantly related to the kangaroo rats of our own western states. Our two species are in most cases easily separated, for the **woodland jumping mouse** usually has the tail tipped with white, while the **meadow jumping mouse** never does. Except for differences in habitat preferences as indicated by their

W. H. Burt photo   Courtesy Univ. Mich. Mus. Zool.

Fig. 23.—Meadow Jumping Mouse.

names, the habits of the two species are largely similar. The woodland species, however, is confined to the mountain counties, while the meadow species is state-wide in its distribution.

As would be suspected from its name, the jumping mouse is adapted to making long leaps, and when frightened it progresses in a graceful bouncing fashion sometimes covering as much as eight or ten feet in a single leap! Think how far a man would jump if he could jump twelve times his height. Normally, though, the jumping mouse makes much smaller leaps or merely creeps along as any other mouse would do.

The jumping mouse eats weed and grass seeds, and tender shoots and buds, but seeds are its main fare. In late summer it puts on thick layers of fat and, soon after the first frosts, goes into hibernation in an underground nest for the winter months.

None of our native rats is common enough or widely enough distributed in Virginia to be of any economic importance. The **cotton rat** is of considerable potential importance, but as it reaches the northern edge of its range in the southern tier of counties it is not common in Virginia. In many of the more southern states it is the most abundant rodent, and does untold damage to truck crops, cane fields, and general crops. It is an important enemy of the bobwhite, destroying both nests and eggs and is a serious competitor for food. In the South it takes the place of the meadow mouse as the mainstay of the diet of most predators. It is found in old brushy fields, ditches, and marsh borders, as well as in cultivated areas grown to broomsedge. Its well-beaten trails often form a remarkable network. It is almost as prolific as the meadow mouse.

In the salt and brackish marshes along the bays and rivers of the eastern portion of the State the **rice rat** is a common species. It may also invade dryer land and fresh-water marshes. Because of its habitat it is of scant economic importance with us, although further south it does some damage in rice fields. It is not as prone to make well-defined trails as the cotton rat and is not as prolific as that species. It feeds mostly on the seeds and foliage of marsh plants.

The **wood rat** is common throughout the mountainous portion of the State, occurring most frequently in cliffs, rock slides, and caves, and possibly in some remote areas invading houses. Like its relative the pack rat of the western states, it loves to collect things, and most often about its nests will be found bits of broken glass, bottle tops, buttons, spoons and other trinkets that may have caught its eye. Its nest is a neat globe-shaped structure of shredded grape bark, mosses, grasses, and other appropriate materials, about twelve inches in diameter and with a large entrance in one side. In caves, several nests may often be found within a few inches of one another. Large quantities of food are stored, each item to its own pile, and a food cache may contain a bushel or more of material including such items as walnuts, wild grapes, hickory nuts, bread, cherry pits, and buckeyes. Probably the wood rat does not interfere in any way with the interests of man.

Little need be said about the Old World mice and rats which have become naturalized in our country. Government bulletins and leaflets on control and eradication of these pests are free for the asking. We have been plagued with these unwanted immigrants almost since the first settlements, and not even the potent chemicals like "1080" and "ANTU" give any reason for hope that we shall ever be rid of them. The **house mouse** and the **house rat** are our main worries, for the long-tailed **black rat** usually cannot live in competition with its fierce relative, the house rat. The black rat is very local in its distribution, being common in some sections and entirely absent from others. In many regions these species are serious disease carriers, but apparently they are only a potential menace in this respect in our section. They are probably of more economic importance than any of our native mice and rats.

INSECTIVOROUS MAMMALS

The insectivores are a large and varied group of small mammals which hold the same relation to the world of insects that the carnivores hold to the world of other animals. Although insects provide the chief item in their diet, insectivorous mammals also eat other food. The fisherman bats and fruit bats of the tropics prefer fish and fruit, and the vampire bat is supposed to thrive on blood sucked from its hapless hosts. Most shrews do not hesitate to attack mice and add meat to their diet whenever possible. Generally, however, insectivores live on a diet composed mostly of insects.

Our insectivorous mammals are of two orders: the bats and the shrews and moles. They belong on our list of beneficial mammals, for they do a world of good in destroying insects and do relatively little harm. Moles sometimes become a nuisance by burrowing across prized lawns and golf greens, and bats are popularly supposed to spread bedbugs, but the bug they carry is their own, and not troublesome to man.

Bats are the only mammals which have fully conquered the air. As a matter of fact, they are the only living animals with backbones, besides the birds, which possess the power of true flight. In the prehistoric past there were great flying reptiles which were at home in the air, but these disappeared along with the dinosaurs. The flying lemur, the flying phalanger, the flying squirrel, and the flying fish are all expert gliders, but not one of these is capable of true flight. The bat actually flies, however, and its marvelous performances of aerial gymnastics sometimes rival those of birds, the masters of the air. The fingers of the forelimb of the bat are greatly elongated and webbed with a thin leathery membrane which makes an efficient wing. The toes of the hind foot are not elongated and specialized as are the fingers of the front foot and serve no special function except to hang the bat upside down when it is resting. A membrane, called the interfemoral membrane and similar in texture to the membrane of the wings, is stretched between the two hind legs with the tail projecting backward through the middle. This membrane serves as a rudder to help steer the bat in flight.

Most Virginia bats are small, some are among the smallest of mammals, and the largest has a wing span of only fifteen inches. Not all bats are small, though. One of the large fruit bats of the

52

western Pacific islands, the flying fox, has a wingspread of five feet! Think of having one of these get in your hair! Actually bats do not get in one's hair unless by accident, for they are far more frightened by people than people are by them. They are completely inoffensive creatures and their only thought in the presence of humans is to escape.

Most bats hibernate in caves, in hollow trees, or in buildings during the cold winter months, but some such as the red, hoary, and silver-haired bats migrate from their summer homes to the warmer climate of the South for the winter season. The **red bat** is one of our most conspicuous and best known species. It is easily distinguished from other Virginia bats by its bright red or frosted orange coloration and thickly furred interfemoral membrane. Most of our bats have naked interfemoral membranes. The red bat hangs by day in trees or bushes and takes wing early in the evening in the pursuit of insects. Sometimes it may even be seen abroad during the sunlight hours. It is a slow and leisurely flyer and thus one of the most frequently collected bats. In Virginia, unless he is able to differentiate the various species of bats on the wing, the museum collector is likely to bag a red bat with nine out of ten successful shots. It takes a good shot to hit a flying bat, for they are the most elusive of flying targets, dipping here one second, bobbing there the next, and zigzagging and bouncing more than the gayest butterfly.

Bats can often be identified with a fair degree of certainty by their flight characteristics. For instance, the **hoary bat,** the largest of the eastern bats, may be recognized by its high strong swift flight. Because of these characteristics and because it does not come out until twilight is well advanced, it is one of the most difficult animals to kill, and many collectors get much more thrill and satisfaction from collecting a hoary bat than they do from killing a deer! It is one of the hardiest bats and spends the summer breeding season in Canada and in the northern portions of the United States, making long migratory flights in the spring and fall. Its close cousin, the red bat, holds the migration championship, however, for it has been observed hundreds of miles at sea and is sometimes encountered in Bermuda during migration!

The **silver-haired bat,** with its blackish hairs frosted over with white, is one of our most beautiful species. It apparently has a state-wide distribution but is not often encountered, since it does not usually venture into caves or houses as do some other species; rather, it spends its daytime hours hidden in foliage or in the safety of a hollow tree. As with other bats it displays a peculiar attitude in sleeping. Rather than stretching out comfortably or curling up in a warm ball, the bat chooses to hang upside down when it sleeps. Its hind feet are adapted for clinging to a limb, or a rock, and there it hangs like an animated pendulum, with its wings drooping down and often concealing its face.

The only other Virginia species which roosts characteristically among the leaves or in hollow trees is the **evening bat,** a small

Courtesy Fish and Wildlife Service

Fig. 24.—Little Brown Bat.

brown species somewhat resembling the much commoner little brown bat. The little brown bat and all the other bats occurring in Virginia, other than the four species already mentioned, habitually rest and hibernate in caves or buildings. These cave bats are not as distinctly migratory as the other species and many probably do not migrate at all. Rather than moving south as cold weather approaches, they retreat to the depths of caverns, to attics, or other sheltered places. In these places the bats sleep through the winter with never a fear of the cold, for although it may be below zero outside, the temperature never drops far below freezing in their retreats. Soon after they have begun their winter sleep the body temperature drops considerably and the body may become even chill to the touch. This forces a drastic reduction in the rate of metabolism so that the layers of fat laid on in the fall will be sufficient fuel for the body to use until spring. In that way the bat can safely pass the winter without partaking of a mouthful of food. In the depths of caverns, moisture from the air sometimes condenses on the hibernating bats and stands out in tiny beads over the fur. In the beam of a flashlight these bats glitter like diamonds.

No less than five kinds of little brown bats of the genus *Myotis* might be expected to occur in Virginia. They are all very similar, and are difficult for anyone except an expert to distinguish. The common **little brown bat** and the **Keen bat** seem to be much commoner than the rest, and in Virginia collections have outnumbered the other three kinds several hundred to one. All of these little browns are sociable animals and they often hibernate in closely packed clusters of several hundred or several thousand individuals. Some caves, but none in Virginia that we know of, are famed for their bat rooms where ceilings are literally covered with clusters of thousands of hibernating bats.

In appearance and habits, the **big brown bat** is nothing more than a large edition of the little brown bat, about the size of a red bat. It is not so sociable as its smaller relative and usually hibernates solitarily or in two's and three's. It is the only large bat commonly found in Virginia caves and is the species most often found in the summertime behind window shutters on houses. The only other comparatively large cave bats found in Virginia are the two species of **big-eared bats,** and their enormous ears, almost one-third as long as their total length, immediately distinguish them from any other bats which might be encountered. They have been only very rarely collected in Virginia, so anyone interested in bats should keep on the lookout for them.

How bats are able to fly about in pitch black caverns, or among trees at night, without colliding with obstacles, long remained a great mystery. Then it was discovered that they had been masters of the radar principle long before it was conceived by man. By emitting a continuous series of tiny high-pitched squeaks, far too high-pitched to be heard by human ears, the bat is warned by echoes of obstacles in time to avert them. Their sense is not always

Vernon Bailey photo   *Courtesy Fish and Wildlife Service*

Fig. 25.—Big-eared Bat.

infallible, though, for we have seen them helplessly impaled on barbed wire fences just as dead as other victims which had no radar to guide them.

The least of the cave bats and the last we shall consider is the little

pipistrelle. It is the most completely submissive and inoffensive of all the bats which we have examined, and makes a gentle and interesting pet. It is a sounder sleeper than the other cave bats and often sleeps in the same spot all winter with never a move. Its breeding habits are typical of almost all the bats: its one or two young are born in midsummer, and they accompany the mother on her evening flights during the first few days of their life by clinging tightly to her belly. Then, when they become too heavy for her to carry, they remain in the cave while their mother goes insect catching. After three or four weeks they are weaned and are then able to accompany their mother out into the night on their own wings. Bats in general may bear from one to four young and in some species the young are never carried by the mother in flight.

Before leaving the bats, we should mention that the "bull bat," sometimes popularly classed along with the true bats, is not a bat at all, but a bird, more properly called nighthawk.

Our other insect-eating mammals, the moles and the shrews, belong to the order Insectivora. Of this group the mole is undoubtedly the best known, although shrews are much more numerous. The mole is as well suited for its subterranean environment as the bat is for flight in the air. Indeed, it is better adapted to living underground than any other Virginia mammal. The forepaws have been broadened to make effective scoops for burrowing and the muscles of the shoulders have been enlarged and strengthened to aid in digging. The fur is fine, short, and dense, so as to shed the dirt which would soon coat a less well-adapted animal in the same environment. Having little use for sight in an ever dark world, the mole's eyes have become very small, and are probably of no use except to distinguish between light and dark. The ears are small and concealed in the fur, making the animal more streamlined, and allowing it to proceed more easily through soil. Its snout is elongated and very sensitive to the touch. The mole is one animal that does, literally, "follow its nose."

The nose of the **star-nosed mole** is particularly specialized in this respect, and so peculiar is it that most people are inclined to consider it a freak of nature, especially since it is an animal not often encountered. Actually though, it is not a freak at all. It's just naturally made that way, with twenty-two fleshy pink projections radiating as a rosette around the tip of the snout. It is the only mammal in the world with such a snout. It is not often seen, for unlike the other moles, it prefers a habitat of damp marshy or boggy land. It is a good swimmer and some of its burrows may open into the water. Its burrows are more irregular than those of the other moles and often open to the surface. Thus, if a burrow is traced it is usually found to alternate between surface and subterranean runs many times in the space of a few feet. Earth from the deeper underground runs is pushed up in piles like

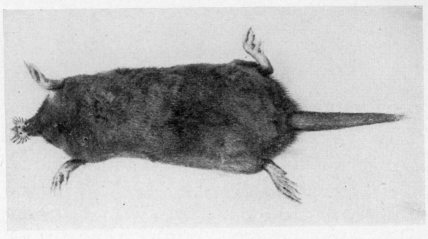

Courtesy Fish and Wildlife Service

Fig. 26.—Ventral view of Star-nosed Mole.

crawfish diggings and these mounds of earth in damp ground often betray the presence of the star-nosed mole. The distribution of this mole in Virginia is not well understood, and interested persons should keep a sharp lookout for it along streams and in other moist places where it might occur. Its range, as we now know it, seems to be peculiarly discontinuous in Virginia. It is rather common in the eastern part of the State near the coast and again in the mountains of the western counties, but is unknown from the wide intervening area.

The purpose of the mole's tunnels is in most cases not for getting from one place to another, but for collecting grubs, beetles, and other insects. The mole is continually making new side passages in search of insects, but it has a few well-developed tunnels which it sometimes uses for years at a time, traversing them at regular intervals to pick up visiting insects. Usually the mole spends its entire life in a limited area, sometimes not venturing more than a stone's throw from where it was born, and it thus has one of the smallest home ranges of all of our mammals.

Most often accused of eating flower bulbs and in general of causing havoc in flower gardens, is the **common mole.** As is often the case with innocent passers-by, it is usually unjustly accused. It likes to venture into flower gardens simply because there in the soft rich earth are found more insects and grubs. Thus, the mole is really a friend of the gardener as it is interested only in the insects and doesn't do anything to the tender flower roots except bump its nose into them. The story sometimes doesn't end there unfortunately, for along behind the mole often comes the pine mouse in the ready-made highway, feasting on the exposed roots and bulbs as it goes. The mole is trapped and killed, the pine mouse enjoys a meal, and there the story ends.

Most of the mole's tunnels pass so close to the surface that a little ridge is raised over each one. The "mole hills" can cause serious inconvenience on golf courses and are eyesores on well-kept lawns, but otherwise the mole is almost completely beneficial. Unless we happen to see the earthen mound being pushed up by the mole, we hardly know of its presence except by its burrows, for it seldom comes to the surface during the daylight hours. It must venture out frequently at night, however, for it is a common food of some of the owls. Most moles retreat to their deeper tunnels below the frost line in cold weather, but the star-nosed mole sometimes comes to the surface even during snowy weather, and its tunnels are occasionally seen ridging the snow as though it were soft earth.

The common mole has practically a state-wide distribution, except in higher mountain sections where it is apparently replaced by the somewhat similar **hairy-tailed mole.** We have never found the common and hairy-tailed moles together, although no apparent reason can be seen why they shouldn't occur in the same locality, since they seem to have similar habits.

All three of our moles may be separated from one another by the appearance of their tails. The star-nosed mole, for instance, has a relatively large tail, at least equalling one-third of the total length of the animal, while the tails of the other two moles are short, hardly half as long as the star-nose's. The hairy-tail and the common mole are also easily distinguished. The common mole's tail is flesh colored and practically naked, while the hairy-tailed mole's tail is blackish and thickly haired.

We would like to know a great deal more about the distribution of the moles, and since the tail itself is sufficient for certain identification, there is no reason why any person in Virginia shouldn't be able to help with the problem. This is only one of many examples of valuable aid which laymen could give to scientists. Most cities have one or more amateur bird clubs. Similar mammal groups would be worthwhile.

The shrews are the least known of our mammals. They are all small, hardly larger than the smallest mice, are active only at night, and are very secretive. One may walk through the woods and fields every day for months at a time and never see a shrew, but with good luck, a short glimpse might be had of one crossing the trail ahead. The few instances where we have been able to observe shrews for a few moments are counted as most noteworthy experiences.

Courtesy Fish and Wildlife Service

Fig. 27.—Short-tailed Shrew.

Usually when shrews are accidentally found, it is when they lie dead in the path. Even then, they are often passed by as baby moles, for they do have many of the features of their larger relatives: pointed snouts, soft, thick, shiny fur, and small eyes and ears. The appearance of their forefeet will set them apart from moles in every instance, however, for whereas the forefeet of the mole are much enlarged, both front and back feet of the shrew are about the same size.

Despite their seeming rarity, shrews are among the most widely distributed of our mammals, occurring in every type of habitat from salt marsh to mountain forest, and even in parks and gardens. In some localities they are the most numerous mammals.

The **short-tailed shrews** are our most common kind and they are the group that are often mistaken for baby moles. The bulk of their food consists of insects, but they are ferocious little beasts and more than a match for mice, so they frequently add meat to their diet. All shrews are cannibalistic to a certain extent.

Two species closely allied to the short-tailed shrews are among the smallest mammals in the world. These are the **least shrew** and the **pigmy shrew.** Both are only about three inches long when fully grown, and the weight of the pigmy shrew is less than that of a dime. These tiny creatures, as well as all of our other shrews, are highly nervous and are apparently easily frightened to death by the shock of a sharp noise or a sudden movement. Their little bodies burn up food with amazing rapidity and to compensate, a volume of food more than equal to their body weight must be consumed every 24 hours.

The fourth and last group of shrews occurring in Virginia are the **long-tailed shrews,** characteristically shrews of the forest. They, like the short-tailed shrews, have a state-wide distribution but are by no means as common. They live in and under the leaves and litter which mats the forest floor, as well as under logs and in burrows. They possess a slight but distinct odor which is characteristic of all of our shrews, but most pronounced in the short-tailed shrews. This odor is so noticeable that it can be sometimes detected from the window of an automobile traveling through an area where shrews are abundant. A similar odor is also character-istic of moles.

Shrews are wholly beneficial in their war against insects and are one of the very few groups of mammals which do not conflict in any way with the interests of man.

Courtesy Fish and Wildlife Service

Fig. 28.—Museum Special Mouse trap used for capturing small mammals. (Mead-ow Mouse in trap.)

MARINE MAMMALS

Probably not more than one out of every hundred persons who use this book will ever see a marine mammal in Virginia, yet among this group are our largest and most interesting mammals. In all the years since John Smith put in at Point Comfort in 1607 with the first boatload of Virginians, fewer than three dozen occurrences of marine mammals have been recorded from our shores. An interested person with the opportunity to cruise along our coast or explore our beaches might double this number in a single year!

By marine mammals we mean mammals which spend most or all of their lives in the sea: the whales, the dolphins, the manatees, and the seals. They may live out their entire lives without ever coming in sight of land, and they may rival fish in streamlined body form and in agility in the water, yet they are not related to fish at all but are warm-blooded mammals. Mammals more familiar to us such as the beaver, the muskrat, and the otter are water lovers, but they are not marine mammals. They are terrestrial mammals which spend part of their time in the water. Maybe fifty million years from now these forms too will have specialized and evolved into what scientists in that day will call marine mammals. There is reason to believe that the ancestors of our marine mammals of today were mammals which lived on land at the time when the earth shook from the heavy tread of the great dinosaurs. Perhaps they had just such an aquatic beginning as our muskrat and otter of today. Maybe they found it easier to get their food from the water, or perhaps they found retreat from their enemies by taking to the water, but at any rate, they spent more and more time in the water and less and less time on land, until finally they became completely divorced from their former terrestrial existence and were as much at home in the water as the fishes. The whales and dolphins and manatees became so perfectly adapted to their watery environment that they can no longer return to the land, and air-breathing remains as the only characteristic of their former terrestrial existence. Although the seal is yet able to move about on land by grotesque contortions of its body, it is more at home in the water.

Despite their superficial resemblance to the fishes, these animals possess the attributes which we ascribe to the mammals. They are warm-blooded, nurse their young, and have hair on their bodies. One may look at a whale from end to end and not see a single hair, probably because there aren't any, but examination of an unborn whale would reveal hairs in the form of bristles on several parts of the body.

P. C. Coffman photo   Courtesy Fish and Wildlife Service

Fig. 29.—Mouth of Finback Whale showing baleen. Note blowhole at lower left.

Of all the marine mammals on the State list the order of whales, dolphins, porpoises, and blackfish is by far the most numerous and most deserving of first consideration. In the following pages references to whales will mean all of these mammals, for dolphins and porpoises and blackfish are nothing more than small whales. The use of the word "whale" in everyday speech to infer great size or quantity has a sound basis in fact, for almost anything we may say about whales is in terms of superlatives. As far as is known, the whales are the largest creatures which ever lived on this planet. Even the giant Mesozoic dinosaurs would have to play second fiddle to the whales of our modern seas. The **blue whale** of the circumpolar oceans, for instance, may reach a length in excess of 100 feet and a weight of 150 tons! Think of the tons of food these leviathans must consume to nourish their bodies. And yet, strangely enough, their diet consists of tiny fish and crustaceans, some of which are almost microscopic in size. The mightiest of all beasts subsists on the smallest items of food consumed by any mammal!

Whales feed entirely on animal life and are classified according to their method of feeding. Many whales are equipped with sharp conical teeth, but others have no teeth at all and instead are equipped with whalebone or baleen. Baleen is horny, hardened skin in the form of long narrow plates which hang from the roof of the mouth in parallel rows like the leaves of a book. The inner edges of these baleen plates are frayed into stiff hairs, and the brush-like grid thus formed serves as an effective strainer to

Fig. 30.—Killer Whale.

separate the plankton, or tiny marine invertebrate animals, from the sea water. The baleen plates may be as much as 10 feet long and a mouthful might weigh 2,000 pounds. In feeding, the baleen whale swims open-mouthed through water teeming with tiny organisms. Then, with a mouthful of water, the whale closes its mouth and presses its tongue against the baleen plates, squeezing out the water and leaving the plankton inside to be licked up by the tongue. Some baleen whales, such as the **finback whale,** have coarser baleen plates and feed on larger organisms, including herring, squids, and sardines, as well as crustaceans. It is not unusual for the stomach of this whale to contain as much as a ton of food, and it may consume six or seven hundred good size cod or herring in a single meal. In their eager pursuit of fish, these and other whales sometimes become so engrossed in their quest that they swim into shallow water and are trapped by the falling tide.

Several of the larger whales have thus been stranded on our coast.

Naturally, the whale is found where its food supply is plentiful, and as the distribution of fishes and plankton is largely governed by the temperature of the water, the whale is forced to make seasonal migrations to obtain food. The migrations of some whales carry them from pole to pole, and make them the greatest nomads among all the mammals. Cool waters favor the greatest development of plankton or "sea soup," so whales follow the northward retreat of cool water in the spring and come southward again in the fall. Whales as well as most other marine animals are almost universally absent from the vast oceanic deserts of warm water.

Young are born at two-year intervals during the southern migration and are by far the biggest babies of the animal world. Among the smaller whales the single calf may be almost half as large as its mother at birth, while among the large whales it is about one-fourth the size of its mother. The blue whale calf is about twenty-five feet long at birth and is weaned at the tender age of one year when it has grown to a length of around fifty feet! It reaches sexual maturity in twenty-eight months and has a life expectancy of fifteen to twenty years.

During its younger days the whale calf is in continual danger from the fierce **killer whale,** the "wolf" of the seas. Indeed, many Eskimos firmly believe that the killer is a wolf which has been transformed into whale form by the gods. Traveling in vicious packs, this savage marauder fears no living thing and is more than a match for even the largest whale, despite its diminutive fifteen to thirty foot size. With its strong conical teeth and powerful jaws, it rips and tears at the larger whales until they are literally torn to shreds, and it often swallows seals and dolphins whole. In a single meal it may eat twenty-five or thirty seals! Whole schools of **blackfish** sometimes lose their lives by driving up onto beaches or wallowing into shallow water in their efforts to escape killers.

One would think that a warm-blooded animal not afforded the protection of hair or warm fur would get cold in the chill waters of the Arctic, but this is not the case, for in whales, and in seals as well, the function of hair as an insulator for retaining body heat is replaced by fat or blubber. The thickness of this blanket varies, but among the large whales it may be as great as one to two feet. Thus protected by this efficient insulator, whales have no fear of the coldest climates. Other specializations, too, have better fitted the whales for their aquatic life. Their tails have been flattened to form broad horizontal flukes which through undulation serve as efficient organs of propulsion. It should be remembered that fish, on the contrary, have vertical tail fins and also scales in most cases. These two characteristics will always separate fish with certainty from whales. Another evolutionary development in the whale was the modification of the forelimbs into flippers or fins for use in steering and balancing. In the course of time the hind limbs have degenerated until they are no longer visible on the external surface of the animal, and along with the loss of a hairy covering, the skin glands also disappeared. One of the most interesting developments was the change of position of the nasal openings from the end of the snout, as we see it in all terrestrial mammals, to the top of the head. The purpose of this change was of course to allow the animal to breathe without rearing its snout out of the water. It would seem that a whale dashing along open-mouthed at a speed of ten to fifteen knots in pursuit of a school of fish would surely get water down its windpipe and choke, but Mother Nature has taken care of this, too. The nasal passages, instead of opening into the throat as in land mammals, open directly into the windpipe and lungs. As a result, the mouth and throat have no connection with the respiratory system at all, and the whale can gulp all the water it wants with no fear of choking.

Thus equipped, the whale can compete with fish in all except one important respect. It has no gills and must periodically come to the surface to breathe, or it would drown just as any land mammal would. When the whale arrives at the surface of the water after a dive, it exhales through the nasal opening or "blowhole," and this column of warm exhaled air immediately condenses to water vapor upon contact with the surrounding cool atmosphere. This is the well-known whale "spout"; the thing the old whalers referred to when they shouted down from the masthead, "Thar she blows!," the signal for action. Thus, the popular belief that a whale spouts water is only a misconception. This column of air or spout may rise geyserlike to heights of twenty or more feet or maybe only a foot or so, and may take a variety of forms such as a long narrow column, a thick ellipse, a short forward directed plume, or a twin

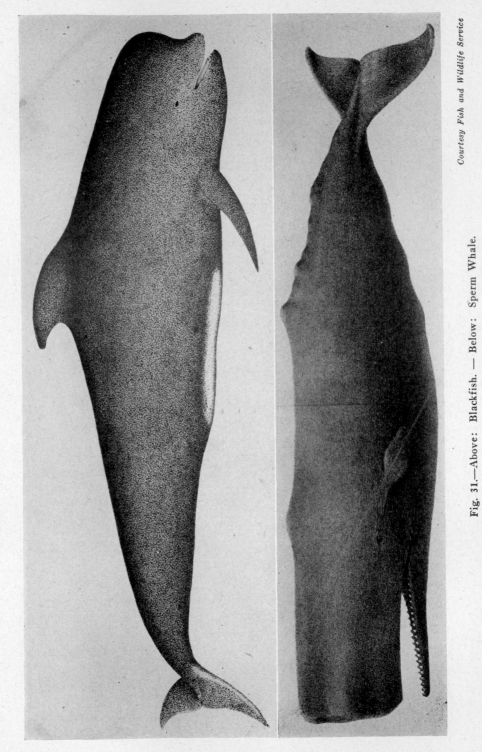

Fig. 31.—Above: Blackfish. — Below: Sperm Whale.

V-shaped column, all according to the shape and form of the blow-hole. In the baleen whales the nasal openings forming the blow-hole are separate, but lie side by side, whereas in the toothed whales the nasal openings are fused into a single blowhole. Whales have

V. B. Scheffer photo   Courtesy Fish and Wildlife Service

Fig. 32.—Cutting blubber from the head of a Sperm Whale. Note tiny lower jaw in comparison to ponderous snout.

the ability to retain large amounts of air in their lungs, and some, like the **sperm whale** which often dives to the ocean floor 2,000 - 3,000 feet below the surface, can remain submerged for fifteen or twenty minutes before returning to the surface for another breath.

In the growing years of our nation the whale held an important place in our national economy. Whale fishing was a major in-dustry and the whaling vessels which set out from Nantucket and

New Bedford carried our flag to every corner of the world. This industry reached its height about 1840, and in the hundred years since has declined to the point where there is almost no whaling in American waters and the whaling fleets which we send to foreign waters are relatively few. There are two big reasons for this decline. First, the whales were slaughtered with no thought of conservation until some species reached the verge of extinction

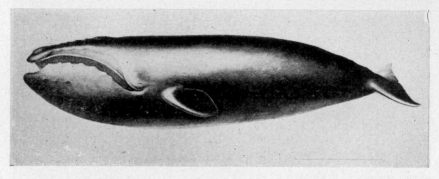

Courtesy Fish and Wildlife Service

Fig. 33.—Right Whale.

and all species became scarce; and second, modern equipment and methods along with the scarcity of whales have drastically reduced the number of whalers who can profitably compete. Kellogg (1940) has theorized that overfishing at the present rate will make it economically impossible to continue large scale whaling operations in the near future.

In the old days when small sailing ships put out from the New England ports on trips that sometimes kept them away from home for three or four years, the **right whale** was abundant, and because of its long, choice baleen and thick blubber, and the ease with which it could be killed, it was considered the "right" whale to pursue. It attained a length of sixty-five feet, and when its blubber was boiled down, the yield of oil from a single individual was sometimes as much as 200 barrels. Whale oil found a ready market, for its clear burning flame made it a favorite fuel for lamps and the best material for candle making. Besides this it was also used as a base for ointment. As the right whale became scarcer and scarcer and the quest for it carried the whaling vessels farther and farther from home, they gradually turned to the pursuit of other species such as the **humpback whale** and the **Pollack whale** which were less productive of the valuable oils and baleen and more dangerous to kill. In those days when the harpoon was hurled by hand from the bow of a small rowboat, the speed and aggressiveness of a whale was something to be taken into consideration!

The invention of the harpoon gun, and still later the development of the explosive-nosed harpoon, brought all the whales to the list of the hunted. Products of the industry were almost as valuable as gold, and slaughter was great. As with all other large animals, reproduction among the whales is slow, calves being born only every other year. Inevitably the millions of whales which once roamed the oceans dwindled until today the last stand of the whaling industry is in the far corners of the Antarctic Ocean. Here large "factory" ships, provided with ramps through which even the largest whales can be pulled on deck, process whales brought in by their subsidiary fleets of small killer ships. International agreements now prohibit the killing of the right whale, the killing of calves and females accompanied by calves, the practice of whaling in tropical calving grounds, and provide for maximum utilization of all carcasses obtained.

Practically every inch of the whale finds a use. The oil is now used in soap making, in the production of glycerine, and in margarine and other edible fats. Kerosene long ago supplanted its use as fuel. A much more valuable oil is obtained from the giant cavity in the snout of the sperm whale. This sperm oil is separated by cooling into spermaceti, a substance used in the manufacture of face cream and other cosmetics, and into a high grade lubricating oil used in the lubrication of fine instruments and light machinery. The head of a single large whale may yield ten to fifteen tons of sperm oil. The intestines of sick sperm whales secrete a fatty substance known as ambergris which in high grade is worth no less than $15 to $20 an ounce. Lumps from a single whale sometimes weigh as much as 750 pounds! This substance is in great demand by the perfume industry where it is used as a fixative or base to hold the expensive essential oils which make perfumes smell and gives them their long lasting qualities. Even the flesh and bones of the whale carcass are used, being ground into fertilizer. Thus there is a by-product from almost every part of the body. In some parts of the world the flesh of the whale is eaten.

Fig. 34.—Baleen (Whalebone) stacked up ready for sale.

Among Eskimos whale and seal blubber are staple winter foods, and it is doubtful whether they could survive without it. In the heyday of the hoop-skirt and the corset, whalebone or baleen used as braces and stays was indispensable and always in great demand. Nowadays its use is almost wholly supplanted by flexible steel.

No discussion of whales would be complete without some mention of Jonah and his troubles. The largest whales of the seas, the baleen whales, have very large mouths. The mouth of the right whale for instance is quite large enough to accomodate a large man. These greatest of animals, though, would have choked to death on a man even as small as Jonah, for their throats are only

H. L. Todd drawing   *Courtesy Fish and Wildlife Service*

Fig. 35.—Pigmy Sperm Whale.

a few inches in diameter. The only whales actually capable of swallowing a man are the smaller killer and sperm whales. The sperm whale, probably the whale which inspired Herman Melville's "Moby Dick," eats large octopuses, seals, and squids as a regular part of its diet. It could easily have finished off Jonah in one gulp.

The small toothed whales, the dolphins, porpoises, and blackfish, are far more numerous than their larger and more celebrated relatives and are likely to be seen with more frequency on Virginia shores. The **bottle-nosed dolphin** and the **common dolphin** are frequently found stranded on the resort beaches as well as in more remote places, and may often be seen capering just offshore. Nine-tenths of the small whales seen in our waters will prove to be one or the other of these two common species. The others which might occur are rare enough to cause considerable excitement among mammalogists when they are discovered. The **beaked whales,** for instance, are hardly known to scientists and are thought to be slowly but surely vanishing from the earth. They have been found on the North Carolina coast and might be expected in Virginia. During World War II the late Glover M. Allen found several mutilated specimens of the rare **pigmy sperm whale** which had washed up on the beach at Cape Henry. He thought probably they had become fouled in the propellers of torpedo boats which were passing through the capes on maneuvers. One of the few North American records for the little known **long-beaked dolphin**

H. W. Elliott drawing   *Courtesy Fish and Wildlife Service*

Fig. 36.—Harbor Porpoise.

is from Norfolk. Several other species, including the **spotted dolphin,** the **false killer,** and the **harbor porpoise,** are not so rare and might be expected in Virginia waters at any time.

Because of their diminutive size, the smaller whales are of little economic significance, unless we take into account their fish-eating habits. Even then, the fish they most commonly eat are not of great commercial value, so they are by no means a menace to our fisheries. Oil from some species of dolphins is used in delicate mechanical instruments. Many of the dolphins travel in sizable schools and have the interesting habit of following ships at sea. They race and frolic and hurdle the bow wave of the ship and in general present a pleasing spectacle.

Persons who are fortunate enough to have the opportunity of visiting the seacoast should keep a sharp lookout for whales, both large and small, which might have been washed onto the beach.

Any specimen found should be carefully checked against the following chart taken from *Natural History,* May 1945.

1. WHALEBONE IN THE MOUTH
(Right Whales)

6. NO TEETH NOR WHALE-
BONE IN THE JAWS
(Narwhal, female)

10. BACK WITH A FIN
(Certain Porpoises
and some whales)

2. TEETH IN BOTH JAWS
(Certain Porpoises
and Dolphins)

7. THROAT SMOOTH
(Black Fish and
other species)

11. BACK SMOOTH
(Right Whales)

3. TEETH IN LOWER JAW
ONLY, BUT MORE THAN
TWO OR FOUR
(Sperm Whales)

12. HEAD ROUNDED
(White Whale, Grampus
and others)

4. TEETH, ONLY TWO OR
FOUR, AT THE END OF
THE LOWER JAW
(Bottle-nose Whales
and other species)

8. THROAT WITH FOLDS
(Finback and Rorquals)

13. HEAD WITH A BEAK
(Dolphins and others)

5. TEETH, ONLY TWO OR
FOUR, IN THE SIDE OF
THE LOWER JAW
(Beaked Whales)

9. BACK WITH A HUMP
(White Whales and
other species)

14. HEAD POINTED
(Pigmy Sperm Whales)

"These sketches illustrate the most useful features for distinguishing the various whales, porpoises, dolphins, etc. They are numbered according to a standard system. This is so that if one of these animals is found stranded on a beach, its characteristics can conveniently be dispatched by letter or wire to the U. S. Coast Guard or to any of the larger biological institutions interested in such matters. The identification can then be made, and the animal can be disposed of or receive scientific attention."

All the features from number 1 through number 14 should be checked, and those applicable to the animal in question should be noted. Generally a combination of two or more features is necessary for specific identification, because thirty-seven recognized species are included in this assemblage of animals. Size and color are valuable additional clues. For example, a whale killed in Mobjack Bay, Gloucester County, in 1856, was forty-six feet long and was entirely black. It had whalebone in its mouth, which fits feature number 1; none of the features 2 through 6 were applicable, but it had a smooth throat, which agreed with feature 7; features 8 through 10 did not fit it, but the back was smooth as in feature 11; none of the remaining features were applicable. Thus, the combination of numbers 1, 7, and 11 would have identified the animal with a fair degree of certainty as a right whale.

The other types of marine mammals which may be found in Virginia waters are very few in number, and of these the **harbor seal** is the most abundant and the most likely to be encountered. It is a small animal, seldom exceeding five feet in length or 100 pounds in weight, and unlike any other marine mammal which might be discovered in our territory, it is covered with a coat of coarse hair and has a pair of hind appendages. Seals are closely related to the carnivores, the dogs and cats, and as seals still retain many terrestrial characteristics, they probably took to the water much more recently than the whales. Several species spend considerable time on land or on ice at the edge of the water, and are able to move about, although with considerable difficulty. In the water, however, they are among the most graceful of all aquatic creatures. They swim by paddling the hind flippers and are swift enough to catch fish, which are the most important item in their diet. Their worst natural enemy is the killer whale, but certain northern seals are among the most important winter foods of Eskimos, polar bears, Arctic foxes, and gulls. Seal skin is used to some extent in handbags and wallets, and oil rendered from seal fat is used as a fine lubricant. The harbor seal, however, does not gather into large schools as do some other species, so it is not commercialized. It is frequently caught in fish nets and may be encountered almost anywhere along the coast, in the bays, or even a considerable distance up the tidal rivers. Like the whales, it is a great wanderer.

The only other marine mammal which has been found in our waters may never be found again. It is the **manatee,** an animal distantly related to the elephants, which is at home in deep quiet tropical rivers and lagoons, where it lives peacefully on a diet of water grasses and other aquatic vegetation. It is a grotesque, cumbersome animal which may weigh as much as 2,000 pounds, and having lost all external evidence of its hind appendages, it is completely helpless on land. Its tail is broad and paddle-shaped and is used to propel it slowly through the water. It is interesting to note that this is possibly the animal which inspired the mermaid legend, for as it stands upright in the water with only its head and shoulders above the surface, it strikes a distinctly human attitude. It is not, however, as beautiful as we are accustomed to think mermaids should be! Unlike the other marine mammals which we have discussed, it cannot stand cold and is killed by temperatures which approach the freezing point. Thus its wanderings are restricted to warm waters, and its occurrence as far north as Virginia and North Carolina may be regarded as accidental.

VANISHED MAMMALS

Part of our mammal fauna is gone forever. Never again shall we see bison roaming our fields or hear wolves howling in the night or hear the eerie scream of the cougar. All these mammals, as well as many others, once abounded within our borders but for one reason or another have passed into oblivion. As for the disappearance of those that have vanished since our country was first settled, man in every case has been at least partly responsible. Though it is regrettable that man has had a hand in the extinction of these creatures, he is not to be blamed too much, for the ascendency of one species and the extinction of another is a regular process of nature which has been repeated over and over again all down through the ages. Probably man did not have much or anything to do with the disappearance of the vast numbers of wild horses, mammoths, mastodons, tapirs, wild pigs, ground sloths, and camels which once roamed our lands, but they are gone nevertheless. As surely as a species of animal comes into being, it is destined to eventual extinction, whether by geologic catastrophies such as volcanic eruptions or earthquakes, or by great climatic changes evolving vast spreading glaciers or desert wastes, or by the hand of man. Our geologists have given us proof of all this by the fossil record in the rocks.

Mammals probably first appeared on the earth during the latter portion of the Triassic period, or approximately a hundred and seventy-five million years ago! Even a hundred and seventy-five million years doesn't seem so long, though, when we stop to think that the earth is probably not less than two billion years old. Mankind, a very recent development, can count only a million years in his history. The first mammals found no broadleaf trees, only conifers, tree ferns, ginkos, cycads, and other palm-like species. There were no flowers and no birds, and these first small mammals must have been very insignificant in a world dominated by dinosaurs. Destiny treated them well, however, and soon mammals had spread from their ancestral home, probably Africa or central Asia, to every corner of the earth.

Our knowledge of prehistoric mammals comes from fossils discovered in caves and in creek banks, or during the excavation of cellars, ditches, cisterns, quarries, or road cuts. Most of the finds have been of single teeth or fragments of bones or skulls. Only rarely have whole skeletons been found. Probably many more fossil remains have been found in Virginia than we have recorded. Whenever bones or teeth are discovered, they should be sent immediately to the National Museum at Washington where they may be studied and classified. A careful record of the character of the soil, the exact location, and if in an excavation, the depth below the surface, should be made when fossils are discovered. Bone does not have to be turned to stone to be a fossil, and the most insignificant looking bone may be of real interest to science.

The most ancient mammal recorded from Virginia was an ancestor of the modern whale, called *Zeuglodon,* which lived during the Eocene epoch. It was long and slender and more like what we think of as a "sea-serpent" than like a whale. Later, during the Miocene epoch, mammals became more numerous or conditions for preserving their remains were improved, and we have more records for Virginia. The remains of several fossil marine mammals indicate that the ocean covered the Coastal Plain about this time. A sperm whale, *Physeter vetus,* two baleen whales, *Balaena palaeatlantica* and *Balaena prisca,* and a dolphin, *Delphinus conradi,* were found in the eastern portion of the State; a seal, *Phoca wymani,* was found at Richmond; and a walrus, *Prorosurarus alleni,* was discovered at Yorktown. All these animals resembled modern species. We now think of camels as "ships of the desert," animals occurring in Africa and Asia and in the Andes of South America, but strangely enough this group of animals seems to have had its origin in North America, and one species, *Procamelus virginiensis,* has been found in Virginia.

As we approach modern times fossils of mammals become much more abundant, and records are available of many species of the Pleistocene epoch, the age of the great glaciers. The fauna must have been interesting, for there were many mammals in our fields and forests which are now known to occur only on other continents. The mastodons, *Mastodon americanus* and *Mastodon progenium,* ancestors of modern elephants, were among the commonest of the larger mammals, and their remains have been found at seven or eight Virginia localities. Another close relative of the elephant, the woolly mammoth, *Mammonteus primigenius,* has been discovered at Saltville, Smyth County. This is the species which was found in such a perfect state of preservation in the Siberian ice a few years ago that dogs feasted on its flesh. It had been in cold storage for at least twenty-five thousand years!

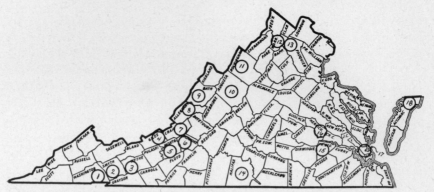

Fig. 37.—Distribution of fossil mammal material collected in Virginia.

1. Washington County, Abingdon: *Mastodon americanus, *Equus complicatus. (Hay 1923).

2. Smyth County, Saltville: *Megalonyx dissimilis, *Equus sp., *Odocoileus, *Cervalces sp., *Bison sp., *Mastodon americanus, *Mammonteus primigenius. (Hay 1923).

3. Wythe County, Ivanhoe: *Megalonyx jeffersonii, Castor canadensis, Neotoma sp., Marmota monax, Peromyscus leucopus, *Tamias laevidens, *Sciurus panolius, Sylvilagus floridanus, Blarina sp., Myotis sp., *Tapirus haysii, *Equus complicatus?, *Mylohyus nasutus, Odocoileus virginianus, *Bison sp., *Ursus amplidens, Procyon lotor, Spilogale putorius. (Hay 1923).

4. Giles County, Newport: Didelphis virginiana, Procyon lotor, Mephitis mephitis, Castor canadensis, Sylvilagus floridanus. Thessalia: Cervus canadensis.

5. Montgomery County, Blacksburg: Peromyscus leucopus.

6. Roanoke County, Kumis: Didelphis virginiana, Neotoma sp.

7. Craig County, New Castle: Didelphis virginiana, Myotis sp., Mephitis mephitis, Marmota monax, Sylvilagus floridanus.

8. Alleghany County, Covington: *Mastodon americanus. (Hay 1923).

9. Bath County, Hot Springs: *Mastodon americanus. (Hay 1923).

10. Augusta County: *Platygonus compressus, *Equus sp. (Hay 1923).

11. Rockingham County, Edom: *Mastodon americanus. (Hay 1923).

12. Warren County, Limeton: *Felis atrox, *Ursus sp., *Tapirus sp. (Clark 1939).

13. Fauquier County, Warrenton: *Elephantidae. (Hay 1923).

14. Halifax County, Denniston: *Equus complicatus. (Hay 1923).

15. Prince George County, City Point: *Mastodon americanus. (Hay 1923).

16. Henrico County, Richmond: *Phoca wymani. (Allen 1880).

17. York County, Yorktown: *Mastodon americanus. (Hay 1923). *Prorosurarus alleni. (Berry and Gregory 1906).

18. Accomac County: Odobenus rosmarus. (Hay 1923).

19. Virginia (no specific locality): *Physeter vetus, *Mastodon progenium; (Hay 1923). *Procamelus virginiensis. (Coues 1877). *Delphinus conradi, *Balaena palaeatlantica, *Balaena prisca. (Leidy 1851 and 1852). *Zeuglodon sp.

*Extinct species.

One of the earliest amateur paleontologists (one who studies fossils) in America was Virginia's Thomas Jefferson. In 1805 Jefferson discovered in a cave in Greenbrier County, West Virginia, the bones of a beast which he erroneously described as belonging to a gigantic lion. What he had actually found was a giant ground sloth, an immigrant from South America, which was as large as an ox and which was a relative of the much smaller tree sloths which still inhabit Central and South America today. Remains of ground sloths, *Megalonyx jeffersonii* and *Megalonyx dissimilis,* have been found in Virginia in Wythe County, and at Saltville, Smyth County.

A bison similar in appearance to the modern species, but somewhat larger, once roamed the western portion of the State, and the horse, *Equus complicatus,* was evidently quite common since its bones have turned up at five Virginia localities. The tapir, *Tapirus haysii,* an animal related to the rhinocerous and the horse, but resembling more closely the pig in general appearance, has been found in Wythe County and in Warren County. Tapirs have changed very little during the tens of thousands of years since they evolved, but occur today only in the tropical forests of Central and South America and in southeast Asia. Two kinds of small pigs or peccaries are known to have occurred in what is now Virginia: *Mylohyus nasutus* in Wythe County and *Plalygonus compressus* in Augusta County. Among the prehistoric carnivorous mammals, only a bear, *Ursus amplidens* (Wythe and Warren Counties), and a lion, *Felis atrox* (Warren County), have been recorded for Virginia. The famous saber-toothed cat, *Similodon,* is unknown from our region. Two extinct squirrels, *Tamias laevidens* and *Sciurus panolius,* have been found in the Wythe County bone caves.

During the age of glaciers many northern mammals were driven far south of their present range. Musk-oxen went as far south as Kentucky and Arkansas, the caribou came into our northern states, wolverines occurred in Maryland and North Carolina and porcupines in Tennessee, and the walrus, *Odobenus rosmarus,* ranged at least as far south as South Carolina. Apparently no remains of any of these mammals, except of the walrus, have been located in Virginia. As for the walrus, the anterior portion of a skull with the tusks partially intact was discovered on the sea beach in Accomac County about 1828. Today this animal is commonly associated with the Arctic Ocean and icebergs and is not known south of the St. Lawrence Estuary. Another northern mammal which occurred in Virginia, possibly during this same period of continental glaciers, was an extinct species of giant moose, *Cervalces*. This specimen was among the material found at Saltville, Smyth County, where no less than seven kinds of large extinct mammals have been discovered. However, the richest Virginia deposits of fossil mammal material yet discovered were located not at Saltville, but in caves near Ivanhoe, Wythe County, by Cope in 1869. Here he identified eight kinds of extinct mammals and ten kinds of recent mammals. The remains of recent mammals are abundant in the limestone caverns of western Virginia, and the V. P. I. Speleological Society with a membership of college students and professors has collected a considerable amount of this recent material, representing at least nine species of mammals ranging from bats and mice to beaver and raccoons.

By recent mammals we mean mammals which have lived since the end of the Pleistocene age, and for which we have historic record. All the mammals which we have discussed up to this point are prehistoric and extinct. Recent times began roughly twenty-five thousand years ago, and had one lived in the year twenty-five thousand B. C., as did our Cro-Magnon ancestors, most of the same mammals seen today could have been observed then. There might have been a few of the last survivors of the Pleistocene fauna such as the woolly mammoth, the royal bison, and the Irish elk, but most of the mammals would have been modern. Since the coming of the white man to America, seven species of mammals have vanished from our State. All of these species, however, still occur in reduced numbers in other parts of America.

The most conspicuous recent mammal which is lost and gone forever from Virginia is the **bison**. Perhaps it is best that it is gone, for a beast of its size and habits would be sadly out of place in our civilization of small fenced farms. When the first settlers came, the bison, or buffalo as it is popularly called, was quite common throughout the State, at least down to the edge of the Coastal Plain, and it left its name for many communities: Buffalo Forge, Rockbridge County; Buffalo Gap, August County; Buffalo Junction and Buffalo Springs, Mecklenburg County; Buffalo Ridge, Patrick County; Buffalo Station, Nelson County; and Forks of Buffalo, Amherst County. Also, there are several Buffalo Rivers and Buffalo Creeks in the State, and the Cow Pasture, Bull Pasture, and Calf Pasture Rivers are said to have been named because of the buffalo which frequented their banks.

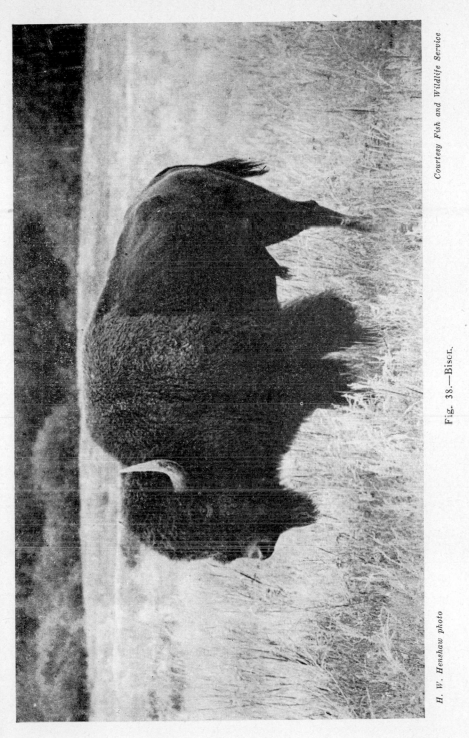

Fig. 38.—Bison.

Captain John Smith probably did not go far enough inland to encounter bison, but many of the other early explorers made mention of them. In June 1613, Sir Samuel Argoll writing of a trip up the Potomac said: "And then marching into the Countrie, I found great store of Cattle as big as Kine, of which the Indians that were my guides killed a couple, which we found to be very good and wholesome meate, and are very easie to be killed, in regard they are heavy, slow, and not so wild as other beasts of the wildernesse." (Purchas: *His Pilgrimes.* Vol. 4, p. 1765. 1625.) William Byrd found them uncommon along the North Carolina-Virginia boundary line which he surveyed, but mentions the killing of a two-year-old near the present site of Danville, on November 11, 1733 (Boyd 1929). Goode (1896) mentions that buffalo still abounded in the vicinity of Charlottesville at the time of Thomas Jefferson's birth, and that a calf captured in the Blue Ridge nearby was presented as a gift to the Governor of the State in 1733. He further stated that "a trail frequented by the buffalo herds crossed the Blue Ridge at Rockfish Gap, twenty-four miles west of Charlottesville, passed the Shenandoah at a ford near Staunton, and afterward over the next range by a passage still known as 'Buffalo Gap,' into the beautiful valleys, then as at present, called the 'Cow Pasture' and the 'Calf Pasture'...."

Coues (1871) recorded what was probably the last occurrence of the bison in Virginia. "The occurrence of the buffalo in Virginia up to the close of the last century, can be substantiated beyond question. Surgeon J. Simpson, U. S. A., who was well acquainted with Nathan Boone (son of Daniel Boone, the pioneer, and then a captain in the service), informs me that he had the fact, in 1843, from Nathan Boone himself, who killed Buffalo in Virginia in 1793,-'97,-'98." The first was killed about 1793 on the Kanawha River (W. Va.), another on New River (probably Va.) in 1797, and the third near the Big Sandy (probably W. Va. or Ky.) in 1798. Thus passed the bison into history as far as Virginia is concerned. Small herds still occur in western Canada and in some of our western National parks, and solitary individuals are kept as curiosities in small parks and zoos throughout the United States, but as a wild animal the buffalo is a thing of the past.

The **elk** was the next large hoofed mammal to follow the bison into extinction from our State and from all the states east of the

Rocky Mountains, the last Virginia specimen being killed in January 1855 by Colonel Joseph Tuley of Clarke County. Elk have since been re-established with Yellowstone stock in Giles and Bland Counties and in Botetourt and Bedford Counties, but with civilization slowly encroaching on the already restricted ranges, its future as a game animal is in doubt. It is not hard to believe that it may soon become a curiosity like the bison.

Probably the next mammal to go was the **fisher,** but it went so quietly that no one missed it. As a matter of fact, very few men were sure that it even occurred in Virginia, since it is an animal of the dense forest and seldom seen by man. It probably preferred the spruce and fir forests on the highest ridges, and when they were destroyed the fisher disappeared. The fisher is a powerful weasel the size of a fox, and is often called "black fox" because of its dark coloration and resemblance to a fox. It is the largest and most powerful weasel that has ever occurred in Virginia as far as we know, and is more than a match for any animal in the forest up to the size of a deer. One of its main items of food is the squirrel as it is an agile climber. Belieing its name, it probably subsisted more on small mammals than on fish. It is one of the few mammals which can prey upon the porcupine with impunity. In the East the fisher is now confined to the wildest portions of the New England States, the Adirondack Mountains of New York, and possibly the northern peninsula of Michigan. Since its soft fur is highly prized and it is an animal easily trapped, man is its mortal enemy. Virginia was near the southern fringe of its range so it is doubtful that trapping had much to do with its disappearance here. It was probably never common in Virginia, and Audubon and Bachman are the only men who left us a definite record of its occurrence. They observed one in pursuit of a squirrel on Peter's Mountain, near Narrows, Giles County, in July 1839, and left an interesting account of the experience in their "Quadrupeds of North America" (1849). The fisher may have occurred in Highland County until the 1890's but there is no authentic record for that area.

Audubon and Bachman sought in vain for one of the fisher's close relatives, the **pine marten,** in the mountains of Virginia, and they were sure that at least a straggler would occasionally occur. Many modern authors give the marten's former range as "south to Virginia," but there seems to be no basis in fact for that statement.

Both the marten and the fisher had small infrequent litters and long gestation periods, the fisher's being almost a year, and this circumstance probably more than any other caused their downfall. Whereas rabbits and squirrels and most other small mammals are very prolific and seem to persist with renewed abundance year after year despite heavy depredations, the marten and fisher were unable to replace losses sustained through trapping and thus vanished from all but the wildest and most inaccessible areas. This characteristic of long gestation periods and small litters is common to most of the larger mammals and accounts for their rapid disappearance before the advance of civilization.

The **porcupine** was another mammal which suffered a fate similar to that of the fisher, for it too reached the southern periphery of its range in Virginia, although it had gone as far south as Tennessee in prehistoric times. It was probably never common in Virginia and Audubon and Bachman (1849) said, "It does not exist in the southern parts of New York or Pennsylvania. DeKay (Nat. Hist. of New York, p. 79) states, that it is found in the northern parts of Virginia and Kentucky. We however sought for it without success in the mountains of Virginia, and could never hear of its existence in Kentucky." Nevertheless, it does occur in parts of Pennsylvania even today, and John Clayton of Gloucester County mentioned in a letter dated March 21, 1739 (Virginia Historical Magazine, Vol. 7, pp. 172-174, 1899) that he had seen two porcupines which had been killed in Virginia. He mentioned no specific locality, but since penetration into what is now West Virginia had hardly begun at that early date, it seems safe to conclude that the porcupines which he saw were from Virginia. Prof. W. D. Saunders of V. P. I. has told us that he saw a porcupine that was killed by 'possum hunters some years ago in Franklin County. This occurrence is probably explained as an animal escaped from captivity similar to Lewis' (1941) Amelia County case. The latter porcupine proved to be an animal which had been brought in by tourists from New Mexico.

Timber wolves once abounded throughout the State and were still present in some localities as recently as fifty years ago. Captain John Smith mentioned the occurrence of wolves near Jamestown (Arber 1910), and Clayton (1694) writing of the same vicinity stated that, "Wolves there are great store; you may hear a company hunting in an evening and yelping like a pack of beagles; but they are very cowardly." William Byrd wrote of being kept awake all night along the North Carolina-Virginia boundary line by the howl'ng of wolves (Boyd 1929), and Daniel Boone is said to have given the name "Wolf Hills" to the site of the present community of Abingdon because of an experience he had there with wolves in 1760 (V. W. Davis, *"Roanoke Times,"* June 2, 1946). *"The Richmond Times-Dispatch"* carried the following item in its May 29, 1938, edition: "The enterprising colonist could make rather a good living back in the days of the seventeenth century by trapping wolves. Such havoc had these animals wrought among sheep that the government offered a bounty for every wolf killed.

"In a court order book for 1696 there is the entry: 'To Colonel William Byrd for four wolves caught in a pitt by his man, Georges, at 300 each is 1,200 pounds of tobacco, 96 cask. To ditto for three killed with a gun by Robin, 200 each.'

"One Henrico levy contains a charge for 1,300 wolves, '200 lbs, each for those killed with a gun and 300 lbs. each for those caught in a pitt.'"

Whether people ever did actually make a comfortable living off of wolf bounties in Virginia is a matter open to question, but bounties nevertheless did remain in force until the wolf was finally exterminated. In an article which appeared in a local paper in February 1936, J. L. Montague, County Agent of Bath County, stated, "The records of the Board of Supervisors of Bath County show that bounties were paid on wolves as late as the year 1881 when Andrew McCarty received a bounty of $5 for one wolf scalp. In 1872, Wm. Deeds was paid $24 for two wolf scalps and in 1870, James Cleek, Sr. received $12 as a bounty on one 'old' wolf scalp. Daniel McCune also claimed a wolf bounty in 1872—One wolf was reported killed in the Falling Springs district in the winter of 1890 in a deep snow." Wolf traps are still frequently discovered in the mountain counties, testifying to the former enterprise of exterminating these animals. Towards the close of the century the wolf became scarcer and scarcer, and was finally pursued into the most remote sections of the State. James H. Watson, in a letter of December 9, 1912, reported two wolves killed in the winter of 1909-'10 on Clinch Mountain, eight miles from Burke's Garden, Tazewell County. This is the last known of wolves in Virginia.

O. J. Murie photo   *Courtesy Fish and Wildlife Service*

Fig. 39.—Cougar.

Wolves reported with increasing frequency in the mountain counties nowadays are without exception either wild dogs or **coyotes.** The real timber wolf of the variety which occurred in Virginia now persists only in Canada and in the northern parts of Minnesota, Wisconsin, and Michigan, while its smaller relative of the Western and Central States, the coyote, or brush wolf, seems to be invading the timber wolf's former range in the Eastern United States. Apparently the coyote can survive where the timber wolf could not. Whether the coyotes killed in Highland, Rockingham, and Grayson Counties in recent years represented part of this apparently spreading population or whether they were merely escapees from circuses or from tourists' cars is impossible to say, but it will be worthwhile to watch for an increase in the number of coyotes in Virginia in the next few years. Probably most of the "wolves" and "coyotes" which harass the mountain sheep flocks are really wild dogs.

About the same time that the wolf was making its last stand in the Virginia mountains, another of the wilderness nobility was disappearing. This time it was the **cougar,** or mountain lion as it is popularly called. It was a formidable animal, sometimes as much as nine feet long, and there are many tales of its ferociousness, most of them evidently exaggerated to fit the animal's size. Wayland (1912) in his history of Rockingham County mentions the following anecdote: "About 1850 Mr. Wynant's mother, a daughter of Rev. John Brown of the Reformed Church, found a panther in the cow stable, and narrowly escaped with her life the beast so nearly catching her as he sprung that he tore part of her clothing." Denbright (1882) related that some darkies hunting raccoons along the Holston River in Washington County treed an animal supposed to be a 'coon, and having shot the animal from the tree, one negro and several dogs were badly injured in the battle which followed—the animal was found to be a panther. Many of the early explorers mentioned encounters with the cougar in their travels through Virginia, and Wm. Byrd complained of the panther's frightful screams along the North Carolina-Virginia boundary line (Boyd 1929). Evidently it once had a state-wide distribution. It was still hunted in the 1880's in the mountain counties, but apparently disappeared soon afterwards. Howell (field notes) reported it in the Blue Ridge country in Rappahannock County in 1911, and it has since been reported in Giles County and in the

Dismal Swamp, but most of these recent observations can probably be credited to overactive imaginations. The subspecies which occurred in Virginia is in all probability now completely extinct.

The last of our native mammals to become extinct was the **beaver.** Its extirpation in Virginia about the year 1910 was accomplished solely by the greed of overtrapping. Fortunately the beaver did not disappear from all eastern states and many successful restockings have been made in Virginia from these sources.

Thus we bring to a close the picture of a passing parade. Just as with men, all mammals have to learn to live together to survive. Down through the ages mammals with conflicting interests have perished, the victor only later to become the vanquished at the hands of a more powerful adversary. Some species have become extinct through conflict among themselves or with some other kind, and some have been wiped out by natural disturbances. In the long history of the earth, none has lived more than a few million years. Faunas, the sum-total of all animal organisms that make up a living picture, are ever changing. Of all the billions of kinds of creatures which have existed on the earth, man is the first and only one which has had the capability of shaping his destiny. We cannot but wonder what effect, if any, he will have on the picture of this passing parade.

THE NATURAL REGIONS OF VIRGINIA

Geographically speaking, Virginia is the southernmost of the Mid-Atlantic States, but from the standpoint of ecology and using mammalian distribution as an indicator, it would seem rather to be the northernmost of the South Atlantic States. No less than eight southern species reach the northern limit of their ranges in Virginia, while not a single northern species finds its southern limit here.

Virginia is sharply divided into eastern and western sections by the barrier of the Blue Ridge Mountains, which wall in many mountain forms in western Virginia and restrict the westward distribution of a few lowland kinds. Within these two natural divisions are several noticeable subdivisions which Fenneman (1938) outlines as follows (See Figure 40): In southwest Virginia, the counties lying along the Kentucky State line are designated as the Appalachian Plateau province and are characterized by several mammals, such as *Synaptomys, Pitymys, Sorex fumeus,* and *Clethrionomys g. maurus,* which are very dark and dull in coloration. Eastward to the Blue Ridge and to the eastern and northern edges of the Tennessee River drainage system is a region called the Tennessee section of the Appalachian Valley province which is characterized by several mammals of large size and dark bright coloration, such as *Clethrionomys g. carolinensis, Tamias s. striatus,* and *Blarina b. churchi.* North of the Tennessee River drainage system and west of the Blue Ridge lies the middle section of the Appalachian Valley province, a region characterized by mammals such as *Clethrionomys g. gapperi* with pale coloration. East of the Blue Ridge to the fall line in eastern Virginia is the Piedmont province, characterized by

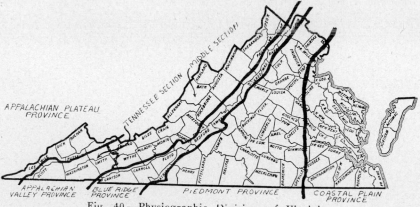

Fig. 40.—Physiographic Divisions of Virginia

91

mammals with pale coloration; *Peromyscus n. lewisi* and *Reithrodontomys h. virginianus,* for example.   Mammals of small size and dark bright coloration, as *Microtus p. nigrans, Peromyscus l. leucopus,* and *Blarina b. carolinensis,* characterize the region known as the Coastal Plain which lies east of the fall line.

It is not surprising that the mammals of the southwest corner of the State and the Coastal Plain, and those of the northern mountain section and the Piedmont should show similar characteristics when we realize that these regions have similar rainfall.   Thus, regions of heavy rainfall are characterized by mammals of dark coloration, whereas drier regions are characterized by mammals of lighter coloration.   Of course, there are many species which do not seem to be much affected by the amount of rainfall and range over several or all of these natural regions without showing any local variations.   The species which do vary according to the climate are among the most interesting pieces in the puzzle of distribution.

CHECKLIST OF THE WILD MAMMALS
OF VIRGINIA

Names in parentheses are of species which are not yet known from Virginia but which are known from contiguous states, and on the basis of availability of suitable habitat may be expected to occur in Virginia.

THE KEYS

The keys are designed to make it possible for persons not too familiar with the kinds of mammals to identify specimens which may come into their hands. If properly used the keys are simple and not the least confusing. They consist of series of paired statements, of which one statement of a pair may be applicable to the specimen in question. Proceed as follows: Read the first pair of statements and choose the one which best fits the animal. If there is a number at the end of the statement chosen, proceed to the pair of statements bearing that number. Suppose, for instance, that the statement is followed by the number (4); then skip the pairs of statements numbered 2 and 3 and choose the statement of the fourth pair which fits the specimen. If this statement is followed by a number, proceed to the pair of statements bearing that number just as before. Sometimes a whole page of statements may be skipped at one jump, but it is important to follow this procedure systematically until identification has been made. When the statement chosen is followed by a name, the specimen has been identified and reference may be made to the page indicated. The animal's name may be found at the end of the first statement that fits, or it may be far down in the key. It will be found that practice facilitates rapid, accurate use of these simple keys.

KEY TO THE ORDERS OF MAMMALS

1. Legs modified as flippers for swimming. (2)
   Legs not modified as flippers. (4)

2. Tail extremely small or missing. Order PINNIPEDIA (seals and walruses), page 144.
   Tail large and horizontally flattened. (3)

3. Tail fish-like, with two divergent flukes or "fins." Order CETACEA (whales, dolphins, and porpoises), page 196.
   Tail not fish-like, but rounded and spatulate. Order SIRENIA (manatees), page 195.

4. Feet hoofed. Order ARTIODACTYLA (deer), page 191.
   Feet not hoofed. (5)

5. Forefeet modified for use as wings for true flight. Order CHIROPTERA (bats), page 113.
   Forefeet not modified for use as wings. (6)

6. Jaws with a total of 50 teeth. (Order MARSUPIALIA (opossums), page 100.
   Jaws with a total of no more than 42 teeth. (7)

7. Tooth rows continuous, and canine teeth or "fangs" large; teeth specialized for eating flesh or insects. (8)
   Tooth rows not continuous, and canine teeth absent; tooth specialized for gnawing. (9)

8. Size large, more then 165 mm. Order CARNIVORA (bears, weasels, skunks, foxes, and cats), page 126.
   Size small, less than 165 mm. Order INSECTIVORA (moles and shrews), page 101.

9. Ear more than 40 mm. long. Order LAGOMORPHA (rabbits), page 186.
   Ear less than 40 mm. long. Order RODENTIA (squirrels, beavers, mice, and rats), page 146.

SYSTEMATIC ACCOUNTS OF SPECIES

In the following pages, all the species of wild mammals which occur or might occur in Virginia are described. The following procedure has been used:

Heading each section are the scientific and common names of the mammal, followed by the name of the man who first described it. To begin the description the type locality is given. This is the place from which came the first specimen described by a scientist in a printed publication. Quite a few mammals were first described from Virginia. Next the characteristics which distinguish the mammal from similar or confusing species are listed, and the measurements of the particular kind or subspecies occurring in Virginia are given. Following are the range or general distribution of the mammal and then its distribution and habitat in Virginia. For each mammal there is an outline map showing by solid symbols the counties from which the authors examined museum specimens and by open symbols the counties from which the mammal has been reported in correspondence or in literature, but from which the authors have not examined specimens. Where more than one subspecies of a mammal is recorded for the State, all are listed under the heading, "Subspecies in Virginia" under a single species name.

The nomenclature and systematic sequence used is that employed by Gerrit S. Miller, Jr., in his "List of North American Recent Mammals, 1923," except in cases where changes of more recent date are in accepted usage. The measurements are given almost entirely in the metric system, the one actually employed in scientific work, but in the case of many of the large mammals, inches or feet have also been included. Millimeters may be roughly converted to inches by multiplying by .04, or inches into millimeters by multiplying by 25.4. To one not familiar with the metric system, the millimeter and inch rules on the back cover of the publication should prove handy.

Class MAMMALIA

Order **MARSUPIALIA**

Family **Didelphiidae**

Didelphis virginiana virginiana Kerr

Opossum

Type Locality.—"Virginia."

Distinguishing Characteristics.—Size medium (678 mm.); ears large and naked; tail long, prehensile, and nearly hairless; legs short; pelage consisting of long coarse hairs and soft underfur. Normally colored individuals have gray, black-tipped underfur and white guard hairs, white face, black but white-tipped ears, white toes and tail, all white except for black base, while a less common color phase has the guard hairs black, giving the animal a very dark appearance. The young are rat-like and have the head white and body black. The female has a marsupial pouch. This familiar animal with its grizzled color and long scaly tail cannot be confused with any other Virginia mammal.

Measurements.—Three adults from Virginia average: Total length, 678 mm. (26.7 in.); tail vetebrae, 296.3 mm. (11.7 in.); hind foot, 63 mm. (2.5 in.).

General Distribution.—Eastern United States from southern New Hampshire, Michigan, and Minnesota south to central Georgia and Mississippi and west to eastern Nebraska and northern Texas; replaced by another subspecies in the Coastal Plain south of North Carolina.

Fig. 41.—Distribution of the opossum, *Didelphis virginiana virginiana,* in Virginia.

Distribution in Virginia.—Abundant in every county. See figure 41.

Habitat.—Woods and thickets, and often venturing out into meadows, cultivated fields and yards in search of food.

100

Order INSECTIVORA

Key to the Order

1. Nose ringed with a cluster or "star" of fleshy projections. *Condylura cristata,* page 103.
   Nose not ringed with fleshy projections. (2)
2. Forefeet large and powerful, much larger than the hind feet. (3)
   Forefeet not large, no larger than hind feet. (4)
3. Tail thin and scantily haired; flesh-colored. *Scalopus aquaticus,* page 102.
   Tail thick and well haired; blackish. *Parascalops breweri,* page 101.
4. Tail equal to more than one-third of the total length. (5)
   Tail equal to less than one-third of the total length. (11)
5. Total length 145 mm. or more. *Sorex palustris,* page 108.
   Total length 135 mm. or less. (6)
6. Tail more than 55 mm. long. *Sorex dispar,* page 106.
   Tail less than 55 mm. long. (7)
7. Tail less than 30 mm. long. *Microsorex hoyi,* page 109.
   Tail more than 30 mm. long. (8)
8. Total length 110 mm. or more. *Sorex fumeus,* page 105.
   Total length less than 110 mm. (9)
9. Coloration bright reddish brown. *Sorex l. longirostris,* page 107.
   Coloration dull dark brown or grayish brown. (10)
10. Occurs in the Dismal Swamp only. *Sorex longirostris fisheri,* page 108.
    Occurs outside the Dismal Swamp only. *Sorex cinereus,* page 104.
11. Coloration brown. *Cryptotis parva,* page 109.
    Coloration black. (12)
12. Fur not glossy; occurs only in the Dismal Swamp. *Blarina telmalestes,* page 112.
    Fur glossy; occurs only outside the Dismal Swamp. *Blarina brevicauda,* page 110.

Family Talpidae

Parascalops breweri (Bachman)

Hairy-tailed Mole

Type Locality.—Eastern North America; supposedly Martha's Vineyard Island, Massachusetts; however, recent collectors have failed to find it there.

Distinguishing Characteristics.—Similar in size and appearance to *Scalopus,* but tail thickly haired and constricted at base; snout somewhat shorter; fur soft but coarser; and color dark slate. It is the only eastern mole with a short, hairy tail.

Measurements.—Seven adults from western Virginia average: Total length, 158.1 mm. (150-169 mm.); tail vertebrae, 29.1 mm. (26-31 mm.); hind foot, 18.7 mm. (18-19 mm.).

General Distribution.—Northeastern United States and adjacent Canada from southern New Brunswick and Quebec south to Ohio and Connecticut and along the Appalachian Mountains to North Carolina.

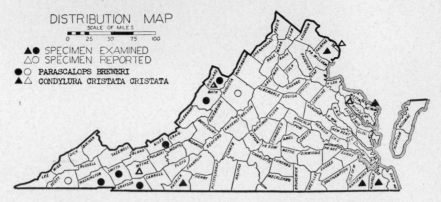

Fig. 42.—Distribution of the hairy-tailed mole, *Parascalops breweri,* and the star-nosed mole, *Condylura cristata cristata,* in Virginia.

Distribution in Virginia.—Apparently common at higher altitudes throughout the western part of the State where it has been taken at elevations of 3000 to 5500 feet. See figure 42.

Habitat.—Prefers loose, light soils, either moist or dry, in spruce and hardwood forests and in meadows and cultivated fields.

Remarks.—We have never captured both *Scalopus* and *Parascalops* in the same locality; apparently their ecologic preferences differ.

Scalopus aquaticus aquaticus (Linnaeus)
Common Mole

Type Locality.—Eastern United States.

Distinguishing Characteristics.—Size small (157 mm.); forefeet greatly enlarged; snout elongated; tail short and naked; eyes and ears small and not visible to superficial observation; fur soft and velvety; color glossy coal black to brownish black. Easily distinguished from other Virginia moles by its short, naked tail and from shrews, which are often erroneously called baby moles, by its greatly enlarged forefeet and much larger size.

Measurements.—Five adults from Virginia average: Total length, 156.6 mm. (153-159 mm.); tail vertebrae, 25.2 mm. (22-28 mm.); hind foot, 19.4 mm. (19-20 mm.).

General Distribution.—The Eastern United States, from Massachusetts and southern New York to southeastern Virginia along the coast, and to North Carolina and Tennessee along the Appalachian Highland.

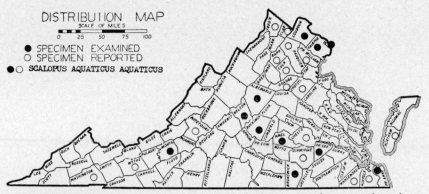

Fig. 43.—Distribution of the common mole, *Scalopus aquaticus aquaticus*, in Virginia.

Distribution in Virginia.—Abundant throughout the eastern half of the State and at lower altitudes in the western portion. We have not taken it at elevations above 2100 feet. See figure 43.

Habitat.—In dry soils of lawns, meadows, cultivated fields, and thin forests.

Condylura cristata cristata (Linnaeus)
Star-nosed Mole

Type Locality.—Pennsylvania.

Distinguishing Characteristics.—Form mole-like; tail long (⅓ total length), scaly and scantily haired; forefeet enlarged; snout fringed with 22 fleshy pink projections; fur thick and silky; color black or brownish black, darkest on back. Immediately distinguished from all other mammals by the peculiar "star" of tentacles fringing the nose.

Measurements.—One adult from Patrick County, Virginia, measures: Total length, 160 mm.; tail vertebrae, 60 mm.; hind foot, 25 mm.

General Distribution.—Southeastern Canada and northeastern United States from Labrador west to Manitoba and south through the Lake States to Illinois, Indiana and Ohio, on the Appalachian mountains to western North Carolina, and along the Atlantic coast to southeastern Virginia and Georgia, being very rare or absent in the intervening coast region of the Carolinas.

Distribution in Virginia.—The star-nosed mole has a peculiarly discontinuous range in Virginia. It occurs in the mountains and in the Coastal Plain but apparently is absent from the intervening Piedmont Uplands. See figure 42.

Habitat.—Damp or marshy situations in fields, woods, and swamps and along sluggish, mud-bottomed streams. Less frequent in dryer uplands.

Remarks.—The presence of this mole may often be detected by its peculiar tunnels which are very irregular and vary from deep subterranean tunnels to surface ridges and open runways all in the space of a few feet. Mounds of dirt, which are pushed up from the deep tunnels and sometimes measure two feet in diameter and six inches in height, are also rather characteristic of the species.

Family Soricidae

Sorex cinereus
Masked Shrew

General Description.—Size small (95 mm.); tail slightly less than one-half the total length; ears hidden in fur. Upper parts dark brown, underparts lighter brown or gray; tail brown above, buffy below; feet whitish.

Distribution in Virginia.—Throughout the mountains at higher elevations and in the Piedmont near Washington.

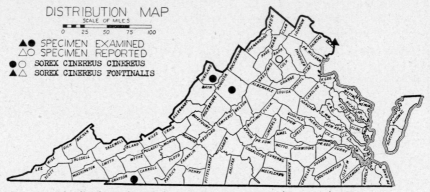

Fig. 44.—Distribution of the masked shrews, *Sorex cinereus cinereus and Sorex cinereus fontinalis,* in Virginia.

Subspecies in Virginia

Sorex cinereus cinereus Kerr

Type Locality.—Fort Severn, Ontario, Canada.

Distinguishing Characteristics.—Distinguished from the subspecies *fontinalis* and from *Sorex longirostris* by larger size; from *Sorex fumeus* by smaller size and darker coloration; and from other Virginia shrews by much longer tail.

Measurements.—Two adults from Grayson and Highland Counties, Virginia, average: Total length, 103.5 mm.; tail vertebrae, 40.0 mm.; hind foot 12.5 mm. These measurements are rather larger than is normal for *cinereus* and a larger series of specimens would probably show the total length to average nearer 95 mm.

General Distribution.—Northern North America including most of Canada from northern Quebec west to central Alaska; south in the Rocky Mountains to northern New Mexico, in the Central States to Indiana and Ohio, and in the Appalachian Mountains to western North Carolina.

Distribution in Virginia.—At high altitudes in the western part of the State, evidently throughout the mountain region, but apparently uncommon. See figure 44.

Habitat.—Around mossy rocks and decaying logs in damp, cool forests of spruce, fir, and birch.

Sorex cinereus fontinalis Hollister

Type Locality.—Cold Spring Swamp, near Beltsville, Prince Georges County, Maryland.

Distinguishing Characteristics.—Similar to *cinereus,* but smaller and with shorter tail. Distinguished from *Sorex longirostris* by much darker coloration and larger size.

Measurements.—Five adults from Maryland (Prince Georges and Dorchester Counties) average: Total length, 92.6 mm. (86-98 mm.); tail vertebrae, 34.6 mm. (31-38 mm.); hind foot, 11.1 mm. (10-11.5 mm.).

General Distribution.—Northern Virginia, eastern Maryland, and southeastern Pennsylvania.

Distribution in Virginia.—Known only from Arlington County.

Habitat.—The Virginia specimens were taken in moist woods around rotting logs resting on a thick carpet of dead leaves and covered with a rich growth of honeysuckle. In Maryland it has been found most frequently in sphagnum bogs.

Sorex fumeus fumeus Miller

Smoky Shrew

Type Locality.—Peterboro, Madison County, New York.

Distinguishing Characteristics.—The largest of the brown long-tailed shrews occurring in Virginia. In the brown summer pelage it superficially resembles *Sorex cinereus* but can be distinguished from it by larger size, particularly of the tail and feet, and by somewhat paler coloration. In the gray winter pelage it resembles *Sorex dispar* but its considerably shorter tail distinguishes it from that species.

Measurements.—Twenty adults from Highland County, Virginia, average: Total length, 115.2 (111-120 mm.); tail vertebrae, 45.3 mm. (40-50 mm.); hind foot, 13.6 mm. (13-14 mm.).

General Distribution.—Southeastern Ontario and central New England south through the Appalachian Mountains to northern Georgia; has also been taken at isolated points in central Kentucky and southeastern Wisconsin.

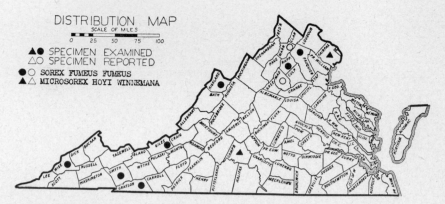

Fig. 45.—Distribution of the smoky shrew, *Sorex fumeus fumeus*, and the pigmy shrew, *Microsorex hoyi winnemana*, in Virginia.

Distribution in Virginia.—Mountains above 2,000 feet elevation. Common to abundant. See figure 45.

Habitat.—Most common in bogs and around rocks and logs in cool, damp woods; less common in other habitats such as dry woods or wet meadows.

Sorex dispar Batchelder

Gray Long-tailed Shrew

Type Locality.—Beedes, Essex County, New York.

Distinguishing Characteristics.—From *Sorex fumeus,* which it most resembles, and from all other Virginia shrews it is distinguished by small size, longer tail, and uniform gray coloration throughout.

Measurements.—One adult from Raleigh County, West Virginia: Total length, 131 mm.; tail vertebrae, 62 mm.; hind foot, 14 mm.

General Distribution.—Known from about fifteen localities in the Appalachian Mountains from New Hampshire and New York south to southern West Virginia.

Distribution in Virginia.—Not known to occur, but should be sought for in the mountains above 2,000 feet elevation.

Habitat.—Cold, damp places such as moist rocks, crevasses between boulders, and moss covered logs in canyons and on talus slopes with northern exposure.

Sorex longirostris
Bachman's Shrew

General Description.—A small long-tailed shrew with coloration reddish brown to fuscous; underparts somewhat lighter than the back.

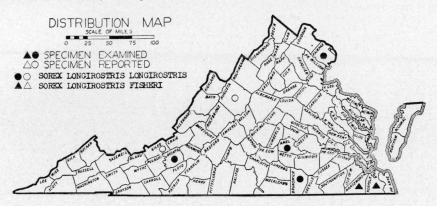

Fig. 46.—Distribution of the Bachman's shrews, *Sorex longirostris longirostris* and *Sorex longirostris fisheri,* in Virginia.

Distribution in Virginia.—State wide.

Subspecies in Virginia

Sorex longirostris longirostris Bachman

Type Locality.—Hume Plantation, swamps of the Santee River (Cat Island, mouth of Santee River), South Carolina

Distinguishing Characteristics.—Small size and reddish brown coloration are characteristic of this shrew; all other Virginia long-tailed shrews have much darker, grayish brown coloration.

Measurements.—Five adults from central and western Virginia average: Total length, 78.2 mm. (72-85 mm.); tail vertebrae, 31.8 mm. (30-34 mm.); hind foot, 10.8 mm. (10-11.2 mm.).

General Distribution.—South Atlantic and East Central States (except in vicinity of Dismal Swamp) from Maryland and Illinois south to northern Florida, and west to the Mississippi River.

Distribution in Virginia.—Probably state-wide, except for the Dismal Swamp, but now known only from the Piedmont Plain and the mountains as far west as Giles County. Uncommon. See figure 46.

Habitat.—In Virginia it has been found most frequently in honeysuckle thickets and in thick grasses and sedges at the edge of ponds or bogs; usually, but not always, in damp situations.

Remarks.—We cannot concur with Dr. Remington Kellogg (1939: 250-251) in his belief that *Sorex longirostris* and *Sorex cinereus fontinalis* are one and the same animal; the reddish brown coloration and small, delicate feet and tail of *longirostris* at once set it apart from *fontinalis*.

Sorex longirostris fisheri Merriam

Type Locality.—Lake Drummond, Dismal Swamp, Virginia.

Distinguishing Characteristics.—"Similar to *Sorex l. longirostris* but much larger with color usually duller above and more tinged with drab or wood brown on the underparts." (Jackson 1928.) Since it is theoretically the only long-tailed shrew found in the Dismal Swamp region, it can be confused with no other mammal in that part of the State.

Measurements.—Three adults from the Dismal Swamp average: Total length 102.7 mm. (98-108 mm.); tail vertebrae, 37.7 mm. (34-40 mm.); hind foot, 12.2 mm. (11.5-13 mm.).

General Distribution.—The Dismal Swamp of Virginia and North Carolina.

Distribution in Virginia.—Known only from the Dismal Swamp where it is evidently fairly common. See figure 46.

Habitat.—Swampy thickets.

Sorex palustris punctulatus Hooper
Water Shrew

Type Locality.—Shavers Fork of the Cheat River, six miles northwest of Durbin, in Randolph County, West Virginia. Altitude, 3600 feet.

Distinguishing Characteristics.—Large size (largest of eastern shrews), long tail, large hind foot, and grizzled coloration distinguish it from all other Virginia shrews.

Measurements.—Three adults from Preston and Randolph Counties, West Virginia average: Total length, 153.3 mm. (152-155 mm.); tail vertebrae, 68.3 mm. (64-71 mm.); hind foot, 19.7 mm. (19-20 mm.).

General Distribution.—"Allegheny Mountains of eastern West Virginia, and probably also of southwestern Pennsylvania, western Maryland, and northwestern Virginia." (Hooper 1942.)

Distribution in Virginia.—Not recorded. Should be sought for in the higher mountains of the western portion of the State. It has been taken in West Virginia barely eleven miles from Highland County, Virginia.

Habitat.—Near moderately flowing streams or rivulets in moist meadows of grass, sedges and annual herbs dotted with willows, birches, hemlocks, or spruces. This habitat can be closely duplicated in numerous bogs in western Virginia.

Microsorex hoyi winnemana Preble

Pigmy Shrew

Type Locality.—Bank of the Potomac River near Stubblefield Falls, four miles below Great Falls of the Potomac, Fairfax County, Virginia.

Distinguishing Characteristics.—Small size (possibly the smallest mammal in the world in respect to weight) and shorter tail will distinguish the pigmy shrew from any other long-tailed shrew occurring in Virginia. It most closely resembles *Sorex longirostris,* but differs from it by having darker (sepia to olive brown) coloration and shorter tail.

Measurements.—The type specimen from Fairfax County, Virginia: Total length, 78 mm.; tail vertebrae, 28 mm.; hind foot, 9 mm.

General Distribution.—Southern Maryland to southwestern North Carolina.

Distribution in Virginia.—Known only from the type locality in Fairfax County and from Altavista in Campbell County. Apparently very rare; one of the rarest of eastern mammals. See figure 45.

Habitat.—One Virginia specimen (the type) was captured in the decayed interior of a fallen log in mixed woods of maple and other deciduous trees; the other Virginia specimen was caught on a dry, wooded hillside amongst scattered rocks and rotting logs in a thick layer of dead leaves.

Cryptotis parva parva (Say)

Least Shrew

Type Locality.—West bank of Missouri River, near Blair, Washington County, Nebraska.

Distinguishing Characteristics.—The combination of extremely small size, short tail, and brown coloration at once distinguish this shrew from all other Virginia mammals. *Blarina b. carolinensis* is similar in form, but larger and glossy black; other small Virginia shrews have long tails equalling nearly half of total length.

Measurements.—Six adults from central and western Virginia average: Total length, 76.5 mm. (70-82 mm.); tail vertebrae, 16.7 mm. (13-19 mm.); hind foot, 10.4 mm. (10-11 mm.).

General Distribution.—Eastern United States, from central New York south to Georgia and west to Nebraska and east Texas.

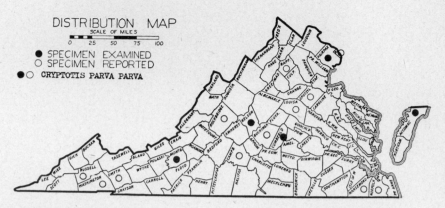

Fig. 47.—Distribution of the least shrew, *Cryptotis parva parva,* in Virginia.

Distribution in Virginia.—The whole State, from sea-level along the coast up to at least 3100 feet elevation in the mountains. Common. See figure 47.

Habitat.—Along the coast it seems to be most common in salt marshes; further inland and in the mountains it is most numerous in deserted fields, although it has also been taken in cultivated fields, thickets, and marshes.

Remarks.—That the barn owl is a most efficient collector of this tiny mammal is well illustrated by the collections made at Blacksburg, Montgomery County. Whereas only six least shrews have been caught in traps in the vicinity of Blacksburg, the remains of over thirty have been taken from pellets picked up beneath a barn owl nest. One pellet alone contained the remains of five *Cryptotis!*

Blarina brevicauda

Short-tailed Shrew

General Description.—A short-tailed shrew, with soft, glossy black fur, only slightly lighter on belly than on back. Most likely to be confused with the mole, from which it may be easily distinguished, however, by much smaller size and by the lack of ponderous forefeet which are characteristic of the mole.

Distribution in Virginia.—The whole State, at all elevations. See figure 48. One of our most abundant mammals.

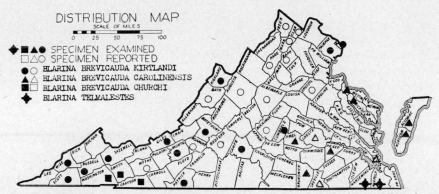

Fig. 48.—Distribution of the short-tailed shrews, *Blarina brevicauda carolinensis,*
Blarina brevicauda churchi, Blarina brevicauda kirtlandi, and *Blarina*
telmalestes, in Virginia.

Subspecies in Virginia

Blarina brevicauda carolinensis (Bachman)

Type Locality.—Eastern South Carolina.

Distinguishing Characteristics.—Small size (93 mm.) and slaty black coloration at once set it apart from other Virginia forms of *Blarina.* It is most easily
confused with *Cryptotis p. parva* which has similar proportions, but *Cryptotis* is
considerably smaller and is brown in all pelages, never black.

Measurements.—Measurements of 34 adults from Amelia County, Virginia,
average: Total length, 93 mm. (86-102 mm.); tail vertebrae, 18.8 mm. (16-22
mm.); hind foot, 12.2 mm. (11-14 mm.).

General Distribution.—The southeastern United States from northeastern
Virginia to central Florida, and westward around the Appalachian Mountains
to Kentucky, Arkansas, and eastern Texas.

Distribution in Virginia.—All of eastern Virginia east of a line drawn
through King George and Prince Edward Counties, except in the Dismal
Swamp, where it is replaced by *B. telmalestes.* See figure 48. Abundant.

Habitat.—Forest, thickets, and fallow fields.

Blarina brevicauda churchi Bole and Moulthrop

Type Locality.—Roan Mountain, Mitchell County, North Carolina.

Distinguishing Characteristics.—Similar to *B. b. kirtlandi,* but larger and
much darker, and the fur showing less gloss. It is the largest short-tail shrew
found in Virginia.

Measurements.—Ten adults from Whitetop Mountain, Smyth and Washington Counties, Virginia, average: Total length, 122.9 mm. (113-136 mm.);
tail vertebrae, 25 mm. (22-28 mm.); hind foot, 15.2 mm. (14-16 mm.).

General Distribution.—The Great Smoky Mountains of North Carolina, Tennessee and Virginia.

Distribution in Virginia.—At this writing known only from Whitetop Mountain. Specimens from other high points farther north such as Mountain Lake show many of the *B. b. churchi* characteristics. See figure 48.

Habitat.—Cool, damp forests. Along with *Peromyscus m. nubiterrae, Clethrionomys g. carolinensis, Glaucomys s. fuscus,* and *Tamiasciurus h. abieticola* it is characteristic of the cloudland forests of the southern highlands.

Blarina brevicauda kirtlandi. Bole and Moulthrop

Type Locality.—Holden Arboretum, Lake and Geauga Counties, Ohio.

Distinguishing Characteristics.—Distinguished from *B. b. churchi* by slightly smaller size and lighter coloration, from *B. b. carolinensis* by much larger size, from *B. telmalestes* by slightly smaller hind foot and glossier pelage, and from all other Virginia shrews by the combination of large size and short tail.

Measurements.—Measurements of 45 adults from Highland and Montgomery Counties, Virginia, average: Total length, 116.3 mm. (105-126 mm.); tail vertebrae, 24.6 mm. (19-30 mm.); hind foot, 14.8 mm. (13-16 mm.).

General Distribution.—From western Virginia, eastern Pennsylvania, and southwestern New York, west to northwestern Michigan, central Wisconsin, and central Illinois.

Distribution in Virginia.—All the western portion of the State west of a line drawn through King George and Prince Edward Counties, except for the high mountains of Washington, Smyth, and Grayson Counties which are inhabited by *B. b. churchi.* See figure 48. Abundant.

Habitat.—Forests, thickets, meadows and cultivated lands.

Blarina telmalestes Merriam
Dismal Swamp Short-tailed Shrew

Type Locality.—Lake Drummond, Dismal Swamp, Norfolk County, Virginia.

Distinguishing Characteristics.—Medium size, dark dull coloration, almost complete absence of gloss on the fur, and long, broad hind feet distinguish *B. telmalestes* from other Virginia forms of *Blarina.*

Measurements.—Measurements of 12 adults from the Dismal Swamp average: Total length, 119.7 mm. (110-128 mm.); tail vertebrae, 26.3 mm. (25-28 mm.); hind foot, 16 mm. (15.5-16.5 mm.).

General Distribution.—Known only from the Dismal Swamp, Norfolk and Nansemond Counties, Virginia, but probably occurs also in adjacent parts of North Carolina.

Distribution in Virginia.—Dismal Swamp. See figure 48.

Habitat.—It is semi-aquatic and has never been found outside its swampy environment, where it is most common in dense undergrowth and cane brakes.

Order **CHIROPTERA**

Key to the Order

1. Interfemoral membrane partially or wholly furred on the upper surface. (2)
   Interfemoral membrane naked. (4)

2. Coloration reddish or orange. *Lasiurus borealis,* page 121.
   Coloration blackish or brownish with the hairs of the back tipped with white.
   (3)

3. Size large, total length more than 125 mm., individual hairs banded. *Lasiurus cinereus,* page 121.

   Size medium, total length less than 110 mm., individual hairs not banded.
   Lasionycteris noctivagans, page 118.

4. Ears reaching at least 5 mm. beyond the end of the nose when laid forward. (5)
   Ears reaching only to the tip of the nose, or less than 5 mm. beyond when laid forward. (7)

5. Ears not conspicuously large. *Myotis keenii,* page 115.
   Ears enormous, equalling almost one-third of the total length. (6)

6. Belly hairs tipped with white; individual hairs of the back black basally.
   Corynorhinus macrotis, page 125.

   Belly hairs pink tipped; individual hairs of the back gray basally. *Corynorhinus rafinesquii,* page 124.

7. Size large, total length more than 100 mm. *Eptesicus fuscus,* page 120.
   Size small, total length less than 100 mm. (8)

8. Coloration light yellowish brown; nose, ears, and flying membranes reddish brown. *Pipistrellus subflavus,* page 119.
   Coloration darker; nose, ears and flying membranes dark brown or blackish.
   (9)

9. Fur short and sparse, not shiny; ears thick and leathery. *Nycticeius humeralis,* page 122.
   Fur long and dense, shiny; ears not thick and leathery. (10)

10. Wing membranes attached to the hind feet at the ankle joints. *Myotis grisescens* page 115.
    Wing membranes attached to the hind feet at the base of the toes. (11)

11. Size small, total length less than 85 mm. *Myotis subulatus,* page 117.
    Size larger, total length more than 85 mm. (12)

12. Coloration pinkish brown; individual hairs tricolor. *Myotis sodalis,* page 116.
    Coloration yellowish brown to reddish brown; individual hair bicolor. *Myotis lucifugus,* page 114.

113

Family **Vespertilionidae**

Myotis lucifugus lucifugus (LeConte)

Little Brown Bat

Type Locality.—Georgia; probably near Riceboro, Liberty County.

Distinguishing Characteristics.—Size small; hairs relatively long and glossy tipped; basal portion of the hairs of back dark and sharply differentiated from the tip; coloration of upper parts varying from dark yellowish brown to olive brown; underparts yellowish brown; face, ears and membranes, dark brown; membranes very sparsely furred or not furred at all; interfemoral membrane arising from base of toes; ears reaching tip of nose or extending 1 or 2 mm. beyond when laid forward. Young individuals are similar but much darker. Distinguished from the other common small brown bats of Virginia as follows: from *Myotis keenii* by much shorter ears, which reach only to tip of nose when laid forward; from *Pipistrellus* by larger size and dark brown rather than light yellowish brown coloration; and from *Nycticeius* by much longer, denser fur and glossier coloration. The slender pointed tragus of *Myotis* will also distinguish it from the two latter species which have the tragus blunt.

Measurements: Fifty adults from Virginia average: Total length, 90.4 mm. (85-98 mm.); tail vertebrae, 36 mm. (30-42 mm.); hind foot, 10.7 mm. (10-12 mm.).

General Distribution.—The entire forested portion of eastern and northern North America from Alaska and Labrador south to Arkansas and Georgia.

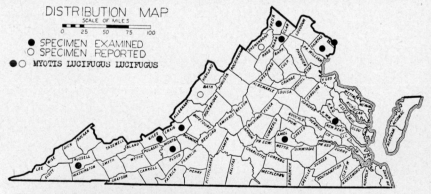

Fig. 49.—Distribution of the little brown bat, *Myotis lucifugus lucifugus,* in Virginia.

Distribution in Virginia.—State-wide; our most abundant bat. See figure 49.

Habitat.—Forested regions; roosting in caves, in the attics of buildings, behind shutters and loose boards, and in hollow trees.

Remarks.—Bats of the genus *Myotis* are extremely difficult for the layman to distinguish, especially since the distinguishing characteristics vary with age, and positive identifications can be made only by experienced mammalogists. However, nine out of every ten Virginia specimens of *Myotis* prove to be *Myotis lucifugus*.

Myotis grisescens   A. H. Howell

Gray Bat

Type Locality.—Nickajack Cave, near Shellmound, Marion County, Tennessee.

Distinguishing Characteristics.—Similar to *Myotis lucifugus* but with individual hairs the same color from base to tip (hairs on all other bats of the genus *Myotis* have the base darkened), and with the wing membrane attached at the ankle joint rather than to the base of the toes as is true in all other small eastern bats. Occurs in two color phases, dusky and russet.

Measurements.—"Average measurements of 25 adults from various parts of the range are: Total length, 88.6 mm. (80.2-96 mm.); tail, 38 mm. (32.8-44.2 mm.); hind foot, 9.9 mm. (8.4-11.2 mm.)." (Hamilton 1943.)

General Distribution.—Limestone regions from eastern Tennessee north and west to Indiana and Missouri and south to western Florida.

Distribution in Virginia.—Not recorded, but should be sought for in the southwestern counties.

Habitat.—So far as known, it is a true cave bat and is never found far from the limestone caves where it roosts and hibernates.

Myotis keenii septentrionalis   (Trouessart)

Keen Bat

Type Locality.—Halifax, Nova Scotia.

Distinguishing Characteristics.—Similar in size and color to *Myotis lucifugus,* but ears much longer, reaching 4 to 5 mm. past the end of the nose when laid forward.

Measurements.—Seven adults from Giles and Montgomery Counties, Virginia, average: Total length, 88 mm. (83-100 mm.); tail vertebrae, 36.1 mm. (32-40 mm.); hind foot, 9.7 mm. (9-10 mm.).

General Distribution.—Eastern North America, from Quebec and Newfoundland west to North Dakota and south to Arkansas and South Carolina.

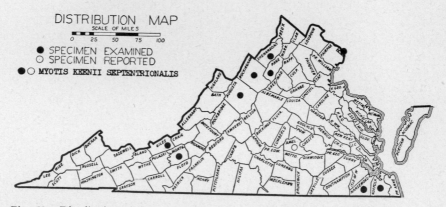

Fig. 50.—Distribution of Keen bat, *Myotis keenii septentrionalis,* in Virginia.

Distribution in Virginia.—State-wide; fairly common. It is often found associated with the common little brown bat, *Myotis lucifugus.* See figure 50.

Habitat.—Forested regions; roosting and hibernating in caves, buildings, and hollow trees.

Myotis sodalis Miller and Allen

Indiana Bat

Type Locality.—Wyandotte Cave, Crawford County, Indiana.

Distinguishing Characteristics.—Similar to *Myotis lucifugus* but differing in the following respects: coloration of upper parts dull cinnamon or chestnut brown; basal portion of hairs of back dull lead color and not sharply distinguished from tip; coloration of underparts pinkish to cinnamon.

Measurements.—Four adults from Giles and Montgomery Counties. Virginia, average: Total length, 90.3 mm.; tail vertebrae, 36.3 mm.; hind foot, 10.3 mm.

General Distribution.—From Maine and Michigan south to Arkansas and Alabama. Known from the Atlantic seaboard only in the northeastern part of its range.

Distribution in Virginia.—*Myotis sodalis* is apparently rare in Virginia, and is known only from Tony's Cave, Giles County; Withero's Cave, Bath County; Madden's Cave, Shenandoah County, and Nellie's Hole, Montgomery County. See figure 51. *Myotis lucifugus* was by far the most abundant bat in each of these caves.

Habitat.—Limestone caves and adjacent areas.

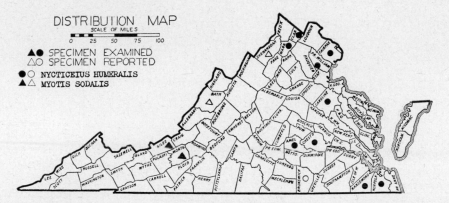

Fig. 51.—Distribution of the Indiana bat, *Myotis sodalis,* and the evening bat, *Nycticeius humeralis,* in Virginia.

Myotis subulatus leibii (Audubon and Bachman)

Least Brown Bat

Type Locality.—Erie County, Ohio.

Distinguishing Characteristics.—Similar to *Myotis lucifugus* but distinguished from it by smaller size, smaller hind foot, and black rather than brown face, ears, and membranes.

Measurements.—Six specimens from Maryland, New York, and Vermont average; Total length, 77.5 mm. (73-82 mm.); tail vertebrae, 32.6 mm. (29.8-35.2 mm.); hind foot, 6.8 mm. (6.6-7 mm.).

General Distribution. From Vermont and Ohio south to West Virginia and Kentucky.

Distribution in Virginia.—Not recorded, but should be sought for in the winter time in caves in heavily forested sections of the mountains.

Habitat.—Wild, forested regions, apparently hibernating most frequently in caves in hemlock forests.

Remarks.—The least brown bat should occur in Virginia since it has been found only a few miles away at White Sulphur Springs, West Virginia, so all small dark bats of the genus *Myotis* should be carefully examined for the characteristics of this species.

Lasionycteris noctivagans   (LeConte)
Silver-haired Bat

Type Locality.—Eastern United States.

Distinguishing Characteristics.—Size medium (105 mm.); hairs long and lax; pelage dark brownish black with many of the hairs tipped with white, giving a frosted appearance, especially on the back; individual hairs a solid color except for the white tip; inner and outer surfaces of the ear, including the tragus, nearly naked; interfemoral membrane (dorsal side) usually sparsely haired and not haired clear to the edges; and anterior edge of the underside of the flight membranes only sparsely haired. This, the most beautiful of our bats, is distinguished from all of our other bats, except the hoary and the red, by the white-tipped hairs; dark coloration immediately separates it from the red bat, and the unbanded hairs separate it from the hoary.

Measurements.—Four adults from Virginia average: Total length, 105 mm. (100-108 mm.); tail vertebrae, 36.3 mm. (28-42 mm.); hind foot, 10.3 mm. (8-12 mm.).

General Distribution.—North America from the Atlantic to the Pacific and from the northern limit of trees south to California, New Mexico and Georgia. It is migratory and probably does not breed in the United States south of the northern tier of states, except in the higher mountains.

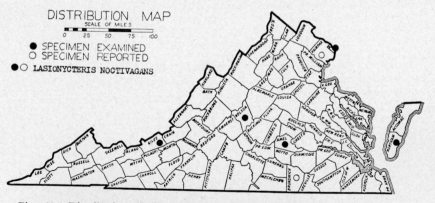

Fig. 52.—Distribution of the silver-haired bat, *Lasionycteris noctivagans,* in Virginia.

Distribution in Virginia.—It occurs from the coastal islands to the highest mountains and is probably fairly common although rarely collected. Over most of the State it occurs only as a migrant in spring and fall, but it probably breeds in the western mountainous section. See figure 52.

Habitat.—Most frequently along ponds and watercourses in wooded regions. Roosts under hanging bark, in hollow trees, in dense foliage, and sometimes in buildings.

Pipistrellus subflavus subflavus (F. Cuvier)
Pipistrelle

Type Locality.—Eastern United States, probably Georgia.

Distinguishing Characteristics.—Easily distinguished from all other eastern bats by very small size and pale yellowish brown coloration. The ears and flying membranes are reddish brown; hairs are tricolored, giving a grizzled effect; ears reach end of nose when laid forward; tragus is blunt.

Measurements.—Sixty adults from various parts of Virginia average: Total length, 84 mm. (76-95 mm.); tail vertebrae, 37.8 mm. (32-46 mm.); hind foot, 9.9 mm. (9-12 mm.).

General Distribution.—Southeastern United States from Maryland west to Wisconsin and Iowa and south to eastern Texas and central Florida.

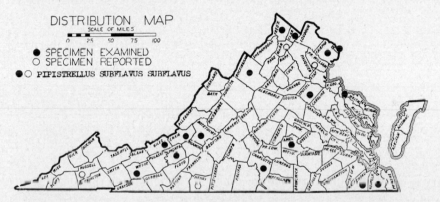

Fig. 53.—Distribution of the pipistrelle, *Pipistrellus subflavus subflavus,* in Virginia.

Distribution in Virginia.—State-wide; one of the commonest of our bats. See figure 53.

Habitat.—Roosts and hibernates in caves and buildings in both wooded and cleared areas.

Remarks.—The pipistrelle is the frailest and daintiest of our bats and in flight the weak fluttering of its wings and its erratic and undulating course might cause it to be mistaken for a large moth. Contrasted with the fierce brown bats (*Myotis* and *Eptesicus*) which bite savagely when captured, the pipistrelle is a very docile and friendly little creature.

A specimen from Giles County was identified as the northern subspecies, *Pipistrellus subflavus obscurus,* by J. K. Doutt of the Carnegie Museum, Pittsburgh, Pennsylvania, but it has not been examined by the authors.

Eptesicus fuscus fuscus   (Peale and Beauvois)

Big Brown Bat

Type Locality.—Philadelphia, Pennsylvania.

Distinguishing Characteristics.—Size large (116 mm.); fur long and lax; ears, wings, and interfemoral membrane thick and leathery; color dark brown. Easily distinguished from all other Virginia bats by large size and uniform dark brown coloration.

Measurements.—Twenty-five adults from Virginia average: Total length, 116.6 mm. (103-130 mm.); tail vertebrae, 44.6 mm. (35-52 mm.); hind foot, 11.3 mm. (9-15 mm.).

General Distribution.—Southern Canada and most of the United States north of Florida, except in the central Rocky Mountains from Colorado to Idaho.

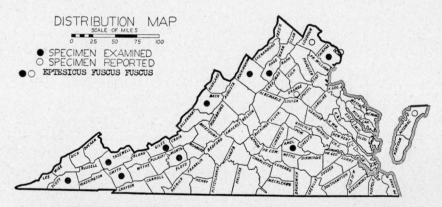

Fig. 54.—Distribution of the big brown bat, *Eptesicus fuscus fuscus,* in Virginia.

Distribution in Virginia.—State-wide; uncommon. See figure 54.

Habitat.—Roosts and hibernates in buildings and in caves in both open and wooded country.

Lasiurus borealis borealis (Müller)
Red Bat

Type Locality.—New York State.

Distinguishing Characteristics.—Size medium (106 mm.); fur long and silky; upper surface of interfemoral membrane densely furred; coloration chestnut to bright orange red with the hairs of the back and breast tipped with white, giving a frosted appearance. Easily distinguished from all other Virginia bats by its rufous coloration and furry interfemoral membrane.

Measurements.—Thirty adults from Virginia average: Total length, 106.2 mm. (92-121 mm.); tail vertebrae, 45.9 mm. (40-55 mm.); hind foot 9.1 mm. (7-11 mm.).

General Distribution.—Wooded portions of Canada and the United States south to Florida and Texas and west to Colorado.

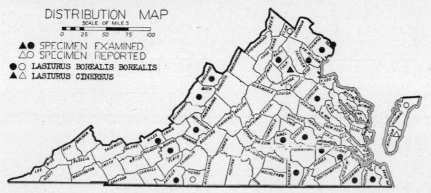

Fig. 55.—Distribution of the red bat, *Lasiurus borealis borealis,* and the hoary bat, *Lasiurus cinereus,* in Virginia.

Distribution in Virginia.—State-wide; abundant. See figure 55.

Habitat.—Forested districts; roosting in the foliage of trees, bushes, corn, etc.

Lasiurus cinereus (Beauvois)
Hoary Bat

Type Locality.—Philadelphia, Pennsylvania.

Distinguishing Characteristics.—Size large (135 mm.); fur long and soft; interfemoral membrane thickly furred; coloration yellowish brown to dark mahogany brown, with the hairs over much of the body banded with black, tan, and dark brown and tipped with white, giving a hoary appearance; inner and outer surfaces of the ear, including tragus, conspicuously furry; anterior edge of underside of wings conspicuously furred for half their length. Easily distinguished from the silver-haired bat and other Virginia bats by its great size, furry interfemoral membrane, and unique coloration.

Measurements.—"Average measurements of 6 adults from various parts of its range are: Total length, 135 mm.; tail, 59 mm.; hind foot, 13 mm.; wing-spread, 400 mm." (Hamilton 1943.)

General Distribution.—Most of North America from the Atlantic to the Pacific and from Mexico to the Arctic Circle; breeding only in the colder parts of its range, mostly north of the United States, but possibly as far south as the Ohio River and the Great Smoky Mountains.

Distribution in Virginia.—It is apparently rare and has been taken only at Cobb's Island, Northampton County, and Raccoon Ford, Culpeper County. It should be sought during the summer months in the higher mountains in the western part of the State. At other seasons it might be expected anywhere in the State. See figure 55.

Habitat.—Forested regions; roosting in the foliage of trees and bushes.

Nycticeius humeralis (Rafinesque)

Evening Bat

Type Locality.—Kentucky.

Distinguishing Characteristics.—Similar to the bats of the genus *Myotis* but easily distinguished from them by its short, sparse, dull brown fur; small short, leathery ears; and blunt tragus.

Measurements.—Two specimens from eastern Virginia measure: Total length, 75-99 mm.; tail vertebrae, 30-37 mm.; hind foot, 8-9 mm.

General Distribution.—Southeastern United States, except in the mountainous sections, from Pennsylvania and southern Michigan south to southern Texas and Florida.

Distribution in Virginia.—Known only from the eastern part of the State in the Coastal Plain and lower Piedmont Provinces, but further collections may show it to occur in the lower portions of the southwestern counties as well. See figure 51.

Habitat.—Wooded districts; roosting and hibernating in hollow trees.

Courtesy Fish and Wildlife Service

Fig. 56.—Specimens of Bats from the Fish and Wildlife Service collection. Left to right: Hoary Bat, Silver-haired Bat, and Red Bat.

Corynorhinus rafinesquii rafinesquii   (Lesson)

Rafinesque's Big-eared Bat

Type Locality.—Lower Ohio River Valley, probably in southern Indiana, or Illinois or western Kentucky.

Distinguishing Characteristics.—Size medium (100 mm.); peculiar glandular masses on nose appear as conspicuous lumps; ears long (about 30 mm.); fur long and lax; interfemoral membrane naked; coloration dark brown above, pinkish buff on the belly; hairs everywhere gray at base and not contrasted with the color of the tips. Distinguished from *Corynorhinus macrotis* by pink rather than white-tipped belly hairs and by gray rather than blackish bases of the hairs. Distinguished from all other eastern bats by the huge ears.

Measurements.—"Average measurements of 11 adults from Pendleton County, West Virginia, are: Total length, 99.8 mm. (96-110 mm.); tail, 45.8 mm. (42-52 mm.); hind foot, 11.5 mm. (11-12 mm.)." (Hamilton 1943.)

General Distribution.—From extreme western Virginia to Kansas and south to Alabama and Louisiana.

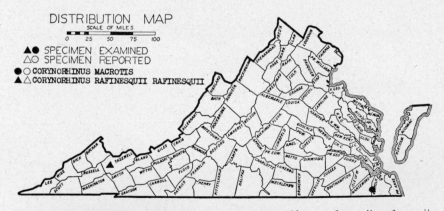

Fig. 57.—Distribution of the big-eared bats, *Corynorhinus rafinesquii rafinesquii* and *Corynorhinus macrotis,* in Virginia.

Distribution in Virginia.—Known only from Burke's Garden in Tazewell County, but should be sought in limestone caves all along the western edge of the State. See figure 57.

Habitat.—Forested regions, roosting and hibernating in caves and hollow trees. Apparently favors the region of semi-darkness in relatively dry caves.

Corynorhinus macrotis (LeConte)

LeConte's Big-eared Bat

Type Locality.—Georgia; probably the LeConte plantation, near Riceboro, Liberty County.

Distinguishing Characteristics.—Distinguished from the very similar *Corynorhinus rafinesquii* by having the belly hairs tipped with white, and by the sharp contrast between the blackish bases and pale brown tips of the hairs of the back. Distinguished from other Virginia bats by its tremendous ears which equal one-third of the total length of the animal.

Measurements.—"Measurements of 4 adults from Tennessee and Georgia average: Total length, 99.5 mm.; tail, 48 mm.; hind foot, 40.2 mm." (Hamilton 1943.)

General Distribution.—Southeastern states from extreme southeastern Virginia westward around the mountains to Kentucky and east Texas.

Distribution in Virginia.—Has been taken only in the Dismal Swamp of extreme southeastern Virginia, but might be expected somewhat farther north in the Coastal Plain. See figure 57.

Habitat.—Wooded regions; roosting in hollow trees and possibly in outbuildings.

Order CARNIVORA

Key to the Order

1. Tail ringed, face masked. *Procyon lotor,* page 128.
   Tail not ringed, face not masked. (2)

2. Coloration black, or black and white. (3)
   Coloration brown or some shade of brown; not black. (5)

3. Tail short and not bushy. *Ursus americanus,* page 127.
   Tail long and bushy. (4)

4. Upper parts marked with four or more white stripes. *Spilogale putorius,* page 135.
   Upper parts marked with no more than two white stripes. *Mephitis mephitis,* page 136.

5. Tail less than one-fourth of the total length. (6)
   Tail more than one-fourth of the total length. (7)

6. Total length less than 250 mm. *Mustela rixosa,* page 131.
   Total length more than 250 mm.; as much as 1000 mm. *Lynx rufus,* page 143.

7. Form dog-like. (8)
   Form not dog-like. (10)

8. Coloration reddish yellow. *Vulpes fulva,* page 138.
   Coloration grayish. (9)

9. Body heavy, wolf-like. *Canis latrans,* page 140.
   Body light, fox-like. *Urocyon cinereoargenteus,* page 139.

10. Total length as much as 9 feet; coloration light yellowish brown. *Felis concolor,* page 141.
    Total length no more than 4 feet; coloration dark brown. (11)

11. Tail very thick and heavy and more than 300 mm. long. *Lutra canadensis,* page 133.
    Tail not thick and heavy; less than 250 mm. long. (12)

12. Coloration of the belly white or yellow. *Mustela frenata,* page 132.
    Coloration of the belly dark brown. *Mustela vison,* page 132.

126

Family **Ursidae**

Ursus american americanus Pallas

Ursus americanus americanus Pallas

Type Locality.—Eastern North America.

Distinguishing Characteristics.—Body large and heavy; toes armed with strong claws; tail short; fur long and soft; pelage glossy black in fall and early spring, often dull in summer; and nose brownish.

A. P. Nelson photo   Courtesy Fish and Wildlife Service

Fig. 58.—Black Bear with cub.

Measurements.—Average specimens measure "about 5 to 6 feet (1500-1800 mm.) in length; tail, 5 inches (125 mm.); hind foot, 7¼ inches (185 mm.); height at shoulders, 25-30 inches (635-760 mm.); weight, 200-500 pounds; skull, about 10 inches (255 mm.) long, 7½ inches (190 mm.) wide" (Lyon 1936). W. N. Haldeman, of Hampton, Virginia, killed a bear in the Dismal Swamp in November 1944 which appears to be one of the largest ever recorded for eastern North America. In a letter to C. O. Handley, he stated that the skull measured 12½ inches in length and 31 inches in circumference (measured at the hinge of the jaw). Before the head was skinned it measured 8½ inches between the ears! Haldeman and his hunting companion could not budge the carcass, much less bring it out of the swamp, so no accurate weight was obtained, but from the size of the head it was estimated that the huge animal must have weighed around 700 pounds. See figure 5.

General Distribution.—Formerly occurred throughout most of forested North America from Labrador south to Georgia and northwestward to Alaska. Now rare or absent in the southern portions of its range, except in the wilder sections.

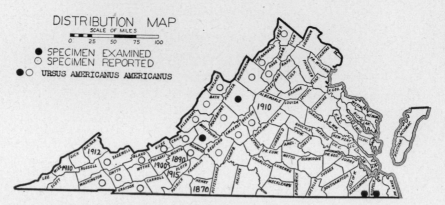

Fig. 59.—Present distribution of the black bear, *Ursus americanus americanus,* in Virginia. Figures indicate approximate dates of extinction in counties where it does not occur today.

Distribution in Virginia.—Formerly state-wide, now restricted to the western mountain counties and to the Dismal Swamp in the southeast. See figure 59.

Habitat.—Woodlands in general, but now especially the wildest, most inaccessible forests and swamps.

Family **Procyonidae**

Procyon lotor lotor   (Linnaeus)

Raccoon

Type Locality.—Eastern United States.

Distinguishing Characteristics.—Size medium (750 mm.); form robust; tail long and bushy and banded with alternate gray and black rings; fur long and coarse and grizzled brown or blackish; face with a black mask across the forehead and eyes. The mask and ringed tail make it impossible to confuse the raccoon with any other Virginia mammal.

Measurements.—Two adult Virginia raccoons measure: Total length, 730 and 800 mm. (30 in.); tail vertebrae, 190 and 277 mm. (9 in.); hind foot, 115 and 119 mm. (4.5 in.). Adult raccoons may weigh from 12 to 25 pounds.

General Distribution.—Southern Ontario, and northeastern United States from Maine south to North Carolina and west to eastern Illinois and southern Michigan.

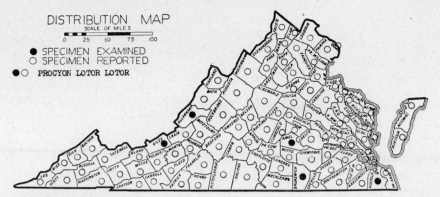

DISTRIBUTION MAP
SCALE OF MILES
0   25   50   75   100
● SPECIMEN EXAMINED
○ SPECIMEN REPORTED
●○ PROCYON LOTOR LOTOR

Fig. 60.—Distribution of the raccoon, *Procyon lotor lotor,* in Virginia.

Distribution in Virginia.—Reported from every county, although it is somewhat rarer in the north and southwest than elsewhere in the State. See figure 60.

Habitat.—Woodlands; most frequent along water courses and in swamps.

Family Mustelidae

Martes americana americana (Turton)

Marten

Type Locality.—Eastern North America.

Distinguishing Characteristics.—Form weasel-like, size a little smaller than a house cat, ears prominent, legs short, tail fairly long and bushy, pelage short and very soft; coloration of upper parts rich yellowish brown, underparts lighter brown, chest and throat orange. The marten may be distinguished from the otter and the fisher by its smaller size and from other Virginia weasels by its larger size, as well as by its distinctive coloration.

Measurements.—Total length, about 600 mm.; tail vertebrae, about 185 mm.; hind foot, about 80 mm.; weight, about 2 pounds.

General Distribution.—Formerly much of eastern North America from Quebec and Hudson Bay south to Minnesota, Ohio, and Pennsylvania. It now occurs only in the wildest, most heavily forested parts of that region, and is extinct in southern New England, and in New Jersey, Ohio, Indiana, and Illinois.

Distribution in Virginia.—Although its range has been given by dozens of authors, even to the present day, as "extending south in the mountains to Virginia," we have been unable to find record of any specific incidence of its occurrence south of Pennsylvania. It is not inconceivable, however, that it might once have occurred in the great spruce forests that formerly covered eastern West Virginia and extended into the Virginia mountains, so we may yet find some long forgotten record of its occurrence in this State.

Habitat.—Deep spruce and pine forests. The marten is largely arboreal.

Martes pennanti (Erxleben)

Fisher

Type Locality.—Eastern Canada.

Distinguishing Characteristics.—Size of fox; form similar to marten; legs short and stout; tail long, cylindrical and rather bushy; ears short; pelage dense and soft; coloration of upper parts black or brownish black shading to gray on neck and face, underparts black. It is aptly described by the name "black fox."

Measurements.—Adult males average: Total length, 965 mm. (38 in.); tail vertebrae, 381 mm. (15 in.); hind foot, 102 mm. (4 in.); weight, 5-10 pounds. Females are smaller.

General Distribution.—Formerly from Maine and Quebec across Canada to southeast Alaska, and south through the mountains in the east to Tennessee and through the mountains in the west to California and Wyoming. In the eastern United States it now occurs only along the Canadian border, where it is commonest in Maine and New York.

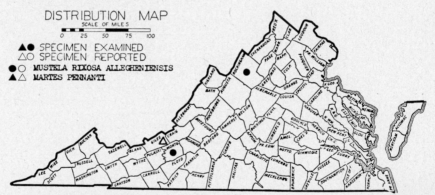

Fig. 61.—Distribution of the fisher, *Martes pennanti*, and the least weasel, *Mustela rixosa alleghaniensis*, in Virginia.

Distribution in Virginia.—Audubon and Bachman (1849, Vol. 1, page 311) have recorded an interesting chase between a fisher and a squirrel which they witnessed on Peter's Mountain, near Narrows, Giles County, in July 1839. We have been told by old residents of the Crabbottom section that "black foxes" had been killed in Highland County as late as 1890, before the spruce was cut out, and it seems reasonable to believe that these may have been *Martes pennanti*. Before the advance of civilization and the resulting decimation of our spruce forests, fishers were probably common in many parts of western Virginia; of course, they are now extinct. See figure 61.

Habitat.—Deep spruce and pine forests. It is even more arboreal than the marten.

Mustela rixosa allegheniensis (Rhoads)
Least Weasel

Type Locality.—Near Beallsville, Washington County, Pennsylvania.

Distinguishing Characteristics.—Size small (198 mm.), smaller even than chipmunk; form lithe and slender; tail very short; coloration of upper parts, including tail, rich walnut brown; chin, throat and lower belly white; mid-belly same as upper parts. Small size and very short tail distinguish *M. rixosa* from *M. frenata,* the only other Virginia weasel of similar build and coloration.

Measurements.—Three adult males from western Virginia average: Total length, 198.2 mm.; tail vertebrae, 34.8 mm.; hind foot, 23.3 mm. An adult female from Montgomery County, Virginia, measures: Total length, 175 mm.; tail vertebrae, 26 mm.; hind foot, 18 mm.

General Distribution.—The Allegheny Mountains from Pennsylvania to North Carolina, and west to Wisconsin.

Distribution in Virginia.—Known only from Montgomery and Rockingham Counties. It probably occurs in all the mountain counties. See figure 61.

Habitat.—In Virginia it has been found in forests, and thickets, along brushy fences, and even in buildings.

Mustela frenata noveboracensis (Emmons)
New York Weasel

Type Locality.—Southern New York.

Distinguishing Characteristics.—Size of small squirrel, but body more lithe and slender; tail fairly long, about ⅓ of total length; legs short; coloration of upper parts dark brown; tail brown with black tip; underparts white or yellow. Distinguished from *M. rixosa* by larger size and longer tail and from *M. vison* by smaller size and lighter coloration.

Measurements.—Seven adult males from Virginia average: Total length, 380.4 mm. (328-452 mm.); tail vertebrae, 124.7 mm. (110-150 mm.); hind foot, 42.3 mm. (38-47 mm.). Females are smaller.

General Distribution.—Southeastern Ontario and the eastern United States from southern Maine south to North Carolina, and west to Illinois and Wisconsin.

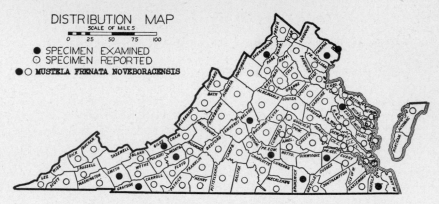

Fig. 62.—Distribution of the New York weasel, *Mustela frenata noveboracensis,* in Virginia.

Distribution in Virginia.—Occurs throughout the State but is not common in the southeastern counties. See figure 62.

Habitat.—Woodlands, thickets, brushy fence rows.

Mustela vison mink Peale and Beauvois

Mink

Type Locality.—Maryland.

Distinguishing Characteristics.—Size large (550 mm.); body long and slender; legs short; tail fairly long and bushy; coloration uniform dark glossy brown over the whole body. Distinguished from *Mustela frenata* by larger size and darker coloration, and from *Lutra canadensis* by much smaller size and smaller tail.

Measurements.—An adult male and an adult female from Rockingham County measured respectively: Total length, 506 and 592 mm. (21.3 in.); tail vertebrae, 189 and 201 mm. (7.7 in.); hind foot, 56 and 69 mm. (2.5 in.).

General Distribution.—Southeastern Ontario and eastern United States from the coast of Maine south to the coast of North Carolina, and inland, except in the high Appalachians, through Pennsylvania, Michigan, Georgia, and Alabama to Missouri.

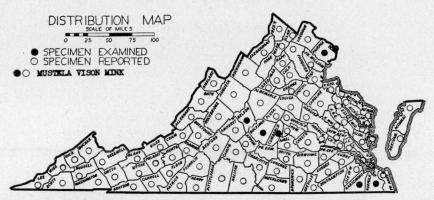

Fig. 63.—Distribution of the mink, *Mustela vison mink,* in Virginia.

Distribution in Virginia. Reported from almost every county. See figure 63.

Habitat.—Along streams in forests and thickets.

Remarks.—References to a black mink in Highland County suggest that the northern subspecies, *Mustela vison vison,* may inhabit the high mountains of the State.

Lutra canadensis

Otter

General Description.—Size large (1000 mm.); body long and slender; head, ears, and eyes small; neck long and stout; legs short and toes webbed; tail long and stout, tapering; fur dense and soft; coloration of upper parts rich glossy brown; underparts, especially lips and throat, lighter brown.

Distribution in Virginia.—Occurs in all parts of the State but is generally rare in the mountains and most abundant in the swamps of the Coastal Plain.

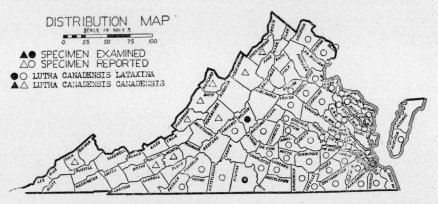

Fig. 64.—Distribution of the otters, *Lutra canadensis canadensis* and *Lutra canadensis lataxina,* in Virginia.

Subspecies in Virginia

Lutra canadensis canadensis   (Schreber)

Type Locality.—Eastern Canada.

Distinguishing Characteristics.—Distinguished from *L. c. lataxina* by darker, more blackish coloration. The large size, long lithe body, long stout tail and neck, and small head will at once distinguish the otter from other Virginia mammals.

Measurements.—Total length, 900-1200 mm. (41.5 in.); tail, 300-400 mm. (13.8 in.); hind foot, 100-120 mm. (4.4 in.). A large otter killed in Rockingham County in 1879 was said to have weighed 15 pounds and measured 3 ft. 10 in. (1168 mm.) in total length.

General Distribution.—From Labrador south to the New England Coast and to Alabama and Tennessee in the Appalachians, and northwest through the Great Lakes States and around Hudson Bay to Alaska.

Distribution in Virginia.—Thought to have once occurred in all the counties west of the Blue Ridge. It has been recently reported in Montgomery, Rockingham, and Shenandoah Counties. See figure 64.

Habitat.—Wooded stream banks.

Lutra canadensis lataxina   F. Cuvier

Type Locality.—South Carolina.

Distinguishing Characteristics.—Similar to *L. c. canadensis,* but considerably paler.

Measurements.—Total length, 900-1100 mm. (39.5 in.); tail vertebrae, 300-400 mm. (13.8 in.); hind foot, 100-120 mm. (4.4 in.). Lewis (1940) reports that the dried (and possibly stretched) skin of an otter killed in Amelia County in 1932 measured 4 feet from tip of nose to tip of tail.

General Distribution.—Coastal Plain and Piedmont provinces of the southeastern United States fron New Jersey south to South Carolina.

Distribution in Virginia.—Counties east of the Blue Ridge. It is most abundant in the great river swamps of the Coastal Plains. See figure 64.

Habitat.—Wooded stream banks and swamps.

Spilogale putorius (Linnaeus)

Allegheny Spotted Skunk

Type Locality.—South Carolina.

Distinguishing Characteristics.—Size about half as great as house cat; form weasel-like but stockier; tail long and bushy; legs short; fur long; coloration of upper parts black, marked with numerous irregular white stripes and spots on the head, back, and flanks; tail black, tipped with white; underparts black. Recognized as skunk by odor; distinguished from striped skunk, *Mephitis,* by smaller size and by numerous white stripes—*Mephitis niger* never has more than two white stripes.

Measurements.—"Seven adult males from Greensboro, Alabama: Total length, 470-563 mm.; tail vertebrae, 193-219 mm.; hind foot, 45-51 mm." (A. H. Howell 1906.) Females slightly smaller.

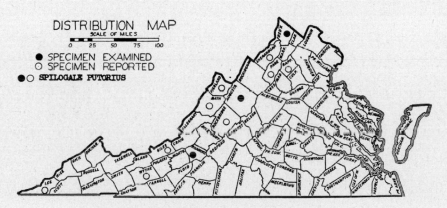

Fig. 65.—Distribution of the spotted skunk, *Spilogale putorius,* in Virginia.

General Distribution.—Southeastern United States from western Florida and northern Mississippi north through Georgia and Tennessee to northern Virginia. Also possibly southern Illinois and Indiana.

Distribution in Virginia.—Throughout the mountain counties. See figure 65.

Habitat.—Rock slides and cliffs in rough, broken, mountain forests.

Mephitis mephitis

Striped Skunk

General Description.—Size of house cat; body stout; tail long and bushy; legs short; fur rather coarse; coloration black, with varying amounts of white in a spot on the forehead and in two lateral stripes running from head to tail. In some individuals the stripes are almost completely lacking, while in others the amount of white almost exceeds the black.

Distribution in Virginia.—Common over most of the State but rare or absent in much of the Coastal Plain.

Fig. 66.—Distribution of the striped skunks, *Mephitis mephitis elongata* and *Mephitis mephitis nigra,* in Virginia.

Subspecies in Virginia

Mephitis mephitis elongata Bangs

Type Locality.—Micco, Brevard County, Florida.

Distinguishing Characteristics.—Distinguished from *M. m. nigra* by longer tail and from *Spilogale putorius* by much larger size.

Measurements.—Total length, 600-700 mm.; tail vertebrae, 250-350 mm.; hind foot, 65-75 mm.

General Distribution.—Along the Gulf Coast from the Mississippi River to southern Florida, along the Atlantic Coast to North Carolina, and in the mountains to West Virginia.

Distribution in Virginia.—The Western and southern portions of the State. The eastern and northern limits of distribution are unknown. See figure 66.

Habitat.—Both cultivated and forested lands.

Mephitis mephitis nigra   (Peale and Beauvois)

Type Locality.—Maryland.

Distinguishing Characteristics.—Similar to *M. m. elongata* but smaller and tail considerably shorter.

Measurements.—Total length, 575-625 mm.; tail vertebrae, 225-250 mm.; hind foot, 60-65 mm.

General Distribution.—Eastern United States from Maine south to northern Virginia, and west of the Appalachian Highland to northern Mississippi, southern Illinois, and lower Michigan.

Distribution in Virginia.—Northern and eastern Virginia, south at least to Powhatan and Chesterfield Counties. Skunks are rare or entirely absent from many of the eastern and southeastern counties. See figure 66.

Habitat.—Forests and cultivated land.

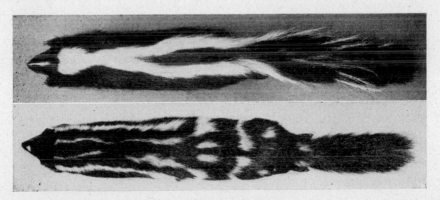

Fig. 67.—Specimens of Skunks from the Fish and Wildlife Service collection. Striped Skunk, above; Spotted Skunk, below.

Family **Canidae**

Vulpes fulva (Desmarest)

Red Fox

Type Locality.—Virginia.

Distinguishing Characteristics.—Size of small dog (1000 mm.); nose slender and pointed; ears large and prominent; tail long and bushy; fur long and soft; coloration of upper parts reddish yellow, darkest along middle of back; feet black; tail yellowish and with a white tip; underparts white. The reddish coloration immediately distinguishes it from the gray fox.

Measurements.—Adults average: Total length, 1000 mm.; tail vertebrae, 360 mm.; hind foot, 165 mm.; weight, 9-12 pounds.

General Distribution.—Southern Ontario and Quebec, and the eastern United States from Maine south along the coast to Virginia and in the interior to Georgia, and west nearly to the edge of the Great Plains.

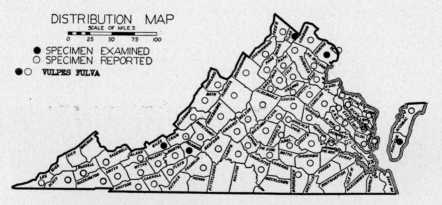

Fig. 68.—Distribution of the red fox, *Vulpes fulva,* in Virginia.

Distribution in Virginia.—Occurs throughout most of the State but is rare or absent from many of the southeastern counties. See figure 68.

Habitat.—Farmlands, open woods, and woods borders.

Urocyon cinereoargenteus cinereoargenteus   (Schreber)

Gray Fox

Type Locality.—Eastern United States.

Distinguishing Characteristics.—Similar in form to red fox but slightly smaller and entirely different in coloration. Upper parts are grizzled, sprinkled with black and shading to lighter gray and finally reddish on the sides; cheeks, throat, and belly whitish; muzzle and chin blackish; tail blackish toward tip.

Measurements.—Five adults from Virginia average: Total length, 906.5 mm. (868-965 mm.); tail vertebrae, 336.5 mm. (280-430 mm.); hind foot, 134.8 mm. (130-139.7 mm.); weight, 8.2 pounds.

General Distribution.—Southeast Ontario and eastern United States from Massachusetts south to North Carolina, and west through Michigan and northern Mississippi to the Mississippi River.

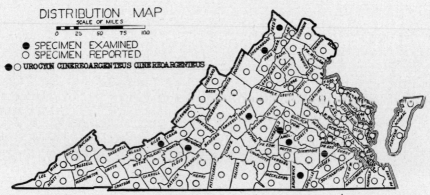

Fig. 69.—Distribution of the gray fox, *Urocyon cinereoargenteus cinereoargenteus*, in Virginia.

Distribution in Virginia.—State-wide; abundant. See figure 69.

Habitat.—Forests and farmland.

Canis latrans latrans Say

Coyote

Type Locality.—Engineer Cantonment, near present town of Blair, Washington County, Nebraska.

Distinguishing Characteristics.—A small wolf with fairly large bushy tail, and long coarse hair; colored grizzled buffy gray on the head, back and tail, yellowish on the muzzle and ears, and white on the belly and throat. Dogs are often so similar in appearance to coyotes or "brush wolves" that it is difficult or impossible for the layman to distinguish between the two with certainty. Often only careful examination of the skull characteristics by an expert can lead to a positive identification.

Measurements.—"Total length, 40-48 inches (1025-1200 mm.); tail vertebrae, 12-15 inches (300-375 mm.); hind foot, 7¼-8 inches (180-200 mm.); weight, 20-45 lbs. (9-20 kgs.)." (Lyon 1936.)

General Distribution.—The central United States and Canada from Ohio westward across the plains through Iowa and Minnesota to Montana and Alberta. Recent records indicate that it may be invading the southeastern United States.

Distribution in Virginia.—Although coyotes have been killed in Rockingham, Highland, and Grayson Counties in recent years, we hesitate to recognize it as an authentic Virginia species since many coyote pups are brought by tourists from the west and are released or escape when they reach maturity. Escapees from carnivals and circuses are also common.

Habitat.—Forests; venturing forth into pastureland and chicken yards at night.

Canis lupus lycaon Schreber

Timber Wolf

Type Locality.—Vicinity of Quebec, Province of Quebec, Canada.

Distinguishing Characteristics.—Form large and powerful; tail long and bushy; pelage fairly long and coarse; coloration grayish cinnamon.

Measurements.—"An adult male from Montebello, Quebec, and one from Algonquin National Park, Ontario, respectively: Total length, 1575, 1626 (mm.); tail vertebrae, 393, 419 (mm.); hind foot, 323, 267 (mm.)" (Young and Goldman 1944). Females are somewhat smaller.

General Distribution.—Formerly probably all of Ontario, southern Quebec, and eastern United States, south possibly to northern Florida and west to Illinois and eastern Minnesota. Still persists in northern Minnesota, Wisconsin, and northern Michigan, and in Ontario and southern Quebec.

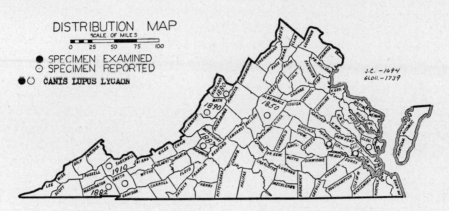

DISTRIBUTION MAP

SCALE OF MILES

0   25   50   75   100

● SPECIMEN EXAMINED
○ SPECIMEN REPORTED
●○ CANIS LUPUS LYCAON

Fig. 70.—Former distribution of the timber wolf, *Canis lupus lycaon,* in Virginia. Figures indicate approximate dates of extermination.

Distribution in Virginia.—Once abounded over the entire State. As far as is known, the last Virginia wolf was killed in Tazewell County in 1910. See figure 70.

Habitat. Now confined to northern forests, but it once enjoyed a wide choice of habitat.

Family **Felidae**

Felis concolor couguar Kerr
Cougar

Type Locality.—Pennsylvania.

Distinguishing Characteristics.—A large powerful cat with long cylindrical tail, short soft fur, and a uniform reddish brown or yellowish brown coloration, except for a white muzzle, a black spot in front of the eye, and a blackish tip to the tail. The large size, long tail, and uniform, unspotted and unstreaked coloration should at once distinguish this animal, yet curiously enough, bobcats and even foxes are repeatedly mistaken for it by untrained observers.

Measurements.—G. M. Allen (1942) gives the following measurements from Vermont specimens: male, total length, about 9 feet; tail, about 3 feet; weight, about 175 pounds. Females somewhat smaller, perhaps measuring about 7 feet in total length.

General Distribution.—Formerly included southern Ontario and the eastern United States from Massachusetts and Vermont south to northern Georgia, and west to northern Arkansas and southern Minnesota. Now probably extinct.

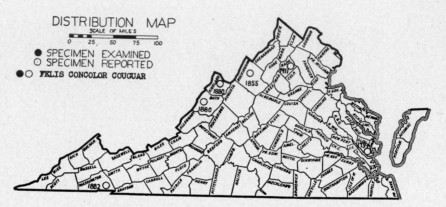

Fig. 71.—Former distribution of the cougar, *Felis concolor couguar*, in Virginia. Figures indicate approximate dates of extermination.

Distribution in Virginia.—Probably once state-wide but now extinct; apparently the last Virginia "mountain lion" was killed in Washington County in 1882. More recent sight records, such as A. H. Howell's field report (Biol. Surv. files) in 1911 from Rappahannock County and an even later report from Giles County, must be looked upon with considerable skepticism. See figure 71.

Habitat.—Forests; especially numerous in broken, rocky country.

Lynx rufus rufus (Schreber)
Bobcat

Type Locality.—New York.

Distinguishing Characteristics.—A medium-sized cat (870 mm.), with a very short tail, and fairly long, loose fur; coloration of upper parts reddish brown, spotted and streaked with black, underparts, white, spotted with black. Can be confused only with the common house cat, from which it is immediately distinguished by its larger size and short, black tipped tail.

Measurements.—Average measurements of 11 adult males from West Virginia: "Total length, 870 mm. (787-935); tail, 146 mm. (133-165); hind foot, 171 mm. (162-195)." (Kellogg 1937.) Weight varies from 10 to 25 pounds. Females somewhat smaller than males. A large cat from the Dismal Swamp is said to have measured four feet long from the nose to the tip of the hind feet (*Washington-Herald,* Nov. 5, 1920).

General Distribution.—Formerly occurred in southern Ontario and Quebec, and in the eastern United States from Maine south to northern Georgia, and west to Iowa and North Dakota. Now absent from the lowlands of its former range south of Pennsylvania and Michigan except in the Dismal Swamp of Virginia. Still common in the southern Appalachians.

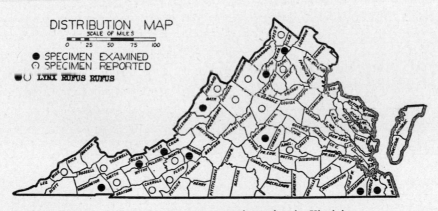

Fig. 72.—Distribution of the bobcat, *Lynx rufus rufus,* in Virginia.

Distribution in Virginia.—Formerly state-wide, but now absent from the lower Piedmont and the Coastal Plain, except in the Dismal Swamp. Common in the mountains. See figure 72.

Habitat.—Heavily wooded or brushy country; especially common in broken, rocky sections.

Order PINNIPEDIA

Family Phocidae

Phoca vitulina concolor DeKay

Harbor Seal

Type Locality.—Long Island Sound near Sands Point, Queens County, New York.

Distinguishing Characteristics.—A small seal with rather coarse pelage; color varying from yellowish gray spotted with dark brown to almost black spotted with yellowish. Distinguished from other seals which might occur in Virginia waters by its small size and conspicuously spotted pelage.

Measurements.—Total length 4-5 feet; weight, 75 to 150 pounds. A specimen from York County is said to have weighed 77.5 pounds and measured 46 inches in total length, and one from Jamestown Island weighed 114 pounds and was 48 inches in length.

General Distribution.—In the Arctic and Atlantic Oceans along the coast of North America as far south as South Carolina.

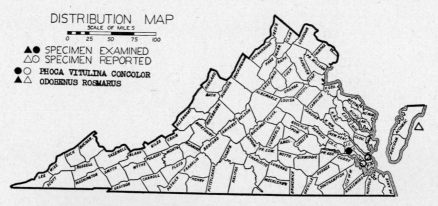

Fig. 73.—Distribution of the harbor seal, *Phoca vitulina concolor,* and the walrus, *Odobenus rosmarus,* in Virginia.

Distribution in Virginia.—Four specimens have been taken in the lower James River, in James City and Warwick Counties, and in the Chesapeake Bay off the mouth of Back River, York County. See figure 73.

Habitat.—Generally found near land about bays, harbors, and river mouths. Sometimes ascends rivers for considerable distance.

144

Family Odobaenidae

Odobenus rosmarus (Linnaeus)

Walrus

Type Locality.—Arctic regions (North America).

General Description.—A very large, seal-like mammal with almost hairless, yellowish brown, wrinkled skin; and large, tusk-like upper canines. Head small; body ponderous; feet in form of flippers; nose blunt and broad. Immediately distinguished from all other aquatic mammals by the long tusks.

Measurements.—"Males about a third larger than females; males 10 to 11 feet in length, weighing from 2000 to 3000 pounds." (Anthony 1928.)

General Distribution.—North Atlantic and adjacent Arctic seas, formerly as far south as South Carolina but not now found south of the St. Lawrence Estuary.

Distribution in Virginia.—The anterior portion of a skull, regarded as being of Pleistocene age, was discovered on the sea beach in Accomac County in 1827. See figure 73.

Habitat.—Cold seas.

Remarks.—Although the walrus has never occurred in Virginia in historical times and indeed probably not since glacial times, it is nevertheless included on this list since the remains which were found at Accomac appear to be identical with those of the modern walrus.

Order **RODENTIA**

Key to the Order

1. Tail horizontally flattened; paddle-like. *Castor canadensis*, page 158.
   Tail not horizontally flattened. (2)

2. Tail more nearly equal to one-half than to one-third of the total length. (3)
   Tail more nearly equal to one-third than to one-half of the total length. (19)

3. Tail bushy. (4)
   Tail not bushy. (7)

4. Skin of sides loose and extended to form membranes used in gliding. (5)
   Skin of sides not loose. (6)

5. Underparts snowy white. *Glaucomys volans*, page 155.
   Underparts buffy or grayish white. *Glaucomys sabrinus*, page 157.

6. Coloration of the upper parts gray, darker along the middle of the back than on the sides. *Sciurus carolinensis*, page 152.
   Coloration of the upper parts gray, buff, or reddish, not darker along the middle of the back than on the sides. *Sciurus niger*, page 153.

7. Tail laterally flattened. *Ondatra zibethica*, page 176.
   Tail not flattened. (8)

8. Upper incisors with longitudinal grooves. (9)
   Upper incisors without grooves. (11)

9. Tail length less than one-half of the total length. *Reithrodontomys humulis*, page 160.
   Tail length more than one-half of the total length. (10)

10. Coloration of the sides orangish; tail often tipped with white. *Napaeozapus insignis*, page 184.
    Coloration of the sides yellowish, tail never tipped with white. *Zapus hudsonius*, page 182.

11. Form rat-like. (12)
    Form mouse-like. (15)

12. Tail length equal to, or more than, half of the total length. *Rattus rattus*, page 178.
    Tail length less than half of the total length. (13)

13. Tail well haired, and not conspicuously scaly. *Neotoma magister*, page 168.
    Tail scantily haired and conspicuously scaly. (14)

14. Tail thick and heavy; has large "Roman Nose." *Rattus norvegicus*, page 179.
    Tail slender; nose not large. *Oryzomys palustris*, page 166.

146

15. Coloration of upper parts yellowish orange; underparts creamy white. *Peromyscus nuttalli,* page 165.

    Coloration of upper parts gray, brown or chestnut; underparts grayish white or brownish. (16)

16. Line of demarcation between the colors of the belly and upper parts not sharp. *Mus musculus,* page 180.

    Line of demarcation between the colors of the belly and upper parts sharp. (17)

17. Tail length usually about one-half the total length. *Peromyscus maniculatus,* page 161.

    Tail length usually slightly less than one-half the total length. (18)

18. Hind foot less than 22 mm. long; body light. *Peromyscus leucopus,* page 162.

    Hind foot more than 22 mm. long; body heavy. *Peromyscus gossypinus,* page 164.

19. Back marked with several longitudinal black and white stripes. *Tamias striatus,* page 149.

    Back not striped. (20)

20. Tail bushy. (21)

    Tail not bushy. (22)

21. Tail equal to no more than one-fourth of the total length. *Marmota monax,* page 148.

    Tail equal to more than one-third of the total length. *Tamiasciurus hudsonicus,* page 150.

22. Tail very short, equal to about one-sixth of the total length. (23)

    Tail only moderately short, equal to about one-third of the total length. (24)

23. Upper incisors with longitudinal grooves; fur coarse. *Synaptomys cooperi,* page 168.

    Upper incisors without longitudinal grooves, fur very soft and fine. *Pitymys pinetorum,* page 175.

24. Back marked with a wide band of dull red from the forehead to the rump. *Clethrionomys gapperi,* page 170.

    Back brown. (25)

25. Size large, total length more than 225 mm. *Sigmodon hispidus,* page 167.

    Size small, total length less than 200 mm. (26)

26. Sides of nose brown. *Microtus pennsylvanicus,* page 173.

    Sides of nose orange. *Microtus chrotorrhinus,* page 174.

Family Sciuridae

Marmota monax monax   (Linnaeus)

Woodchuck

Type Locality.—Maryland.

Distinguishing Characteristics.—Size large (590 mm.); tail short and some-what bushy, not more than one-fourth of the total length of the animal; legs relatively short; fur coarse.   Color above grizzled brown; top of head and face dark brown; feet and legs blackish brown; tail dark brown; underparts somewhat lighter and more scantily haired than upper parts.   The large size, brownish coloration, and short bushy tail serve to distinguish the groundhog from all other Virginia rodents.

Measurements.—"Measurements of eight individuals from Virginia average: Total length, 590 mm.; tail, 142 mm.; hind foot, 86 mm."   (Hamilton 1943.)

General Distribution.—Eastern United States from Pennsylvania and New Jersey south along the coast to Virginia, and in the Appalachian Highlands to northern Alabama; west to Oklahoma and Iowa.

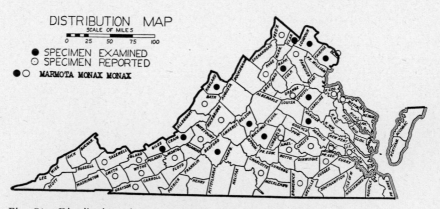

Fig. 74.—Distribution of the woodchuck, *Marmota monax monax,* in Virginia.

Distribution in Virginia.—Common throughout the State except in the southeastern counties, where it is rare or absent from counties east of Brunswick and Prince George. Most common in the mountains. See figure 74.

Habitat.—Open fields, woodlands, cliffs, and caves.

Tamias striatus

Eastern Chipmunk

General Description.—A small striped squirrel with reddish upper parts and white belly. The face, sides, rump, and feet are russet red; a median black stripe bounded on either side by wide gray stripes runs down the back from between the ears to the rump, and white stripes bordered on both sides by black bound the gray. The face is also marked with black, white and buff stripes. The tail is grayish red and not bushy.

Distribution in Virginia.—Throughout the State, but rare or absent in many of the Coastal Plain counties.

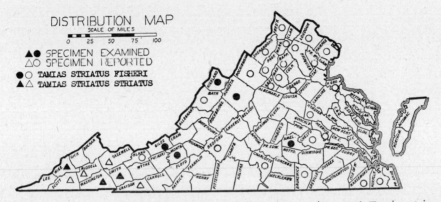

Fig. 75.—Distribution of the chipmunks, *Tamias striatus striatus* and *Tamias striatus fisheri*, in Virginia.

Subspecies in Virginia

Tamias striatus striatus (Linnaeus)

Type Locality.—Southeastern United States.

Distinguishing Characteristics.—Distinguished from *Tamias s. fisheri* by more reddish coloration of rump and sides, and from all other Virginia mammals by the striped back.

Measurements.—Six adults from southwestern Virginia average: Total length, 237.5 mm. (227-254 mm.); tail vertebrae, 84 mm. (80-89 mm.); hind foot, 35.3 mm. (34-37 mm.).

General Distribution.—The southern highlands from southwest Virginia to northern Alabama and from central North Carolina to the Mississippi River.

Distribution in Virginia.—Occurs in more or less typical form in the southwestern counties lying west of the New River watershed. See figure 75.

Habitat.—Woods, thickets, brushy fields, road banks, and outbuildings.

Tamias striatus fisheri Howell

Type Locality.—Ossining, Westchester County, New York.

Distinguishing Characteristics.—Similar in size and appearance to *Tamias s. striatus* but paler; the sides of the body and cheeks paler and more yellowish; the rump duller red; the white stripes more pronounced and less reddish.

Measurements.—Fifteen adults from northwestern Virginia average: Total length, 229.2 mm. (220-248 mm.); tail vertebrae 84.5 mm. (75-92 mm.); hind foot, 34.1 mm. (30-36 mm.).

General Distribution.—Range not well defined by previous revisions of the species, but thought to extend along the Atlantic seaboard from Connecticut to Virginia and through the mountains from southeastern New York to West Virginia.

Distribution in Virginia.—All the State east of the Tennessee River drainage system. Rare in the extreme southeastern counties. See figure 75.

Habitat.—Woods, thickets, fields, roadsides, and outbuildings.

Tamiasciurus hudsonicus

Red Squirrel

General Description.—Size small (310 mm.); tail bushy; pelage fairly long and soft, but not silky; general coloration rufous above, white below. In winter a broad rusty red band extends along the back from the head nearly to the tip of the tail; sides of body and outsides of legs olive gray; ears tufted with black; underparts grayish white. The summer pelage lacks the red dorsal band and is more olive; a distinct black streak along the sides separates the white of the belly from the olive of the back; ears not tufted.

Distribution in Virginia.—Northern and western portions of the State; rare or absent in most of the Coastal Plain and southern Piedmont counties.

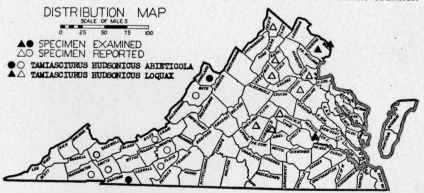

Fig. 76.—Distribution of the red squirrels, *Tamiasciurus hudsonicus abieticola* and *Tamiasciurus hudsonicus loquax,* in Virginia.

Subspecies in Virginia

Tamiasciurus hudsonicus abieticola (Howell)

Type Locality.—Highlands, Macon County, North Carolina.

Distinguishing Characteristics.—Similar to *Tamiasciurus h. loquax* but darker, and the red dorsal band of a deeper shade; the underparts more grayish in winter.

Measurements.—Three adults from Highland County, Virginia, average: Total length, 307 mm.; tail vertebrae, 122 mm.; hind foot, 47 mm.

General Distribution.—The higher portions of the southern Appalachian Highlands from southwestern North Carolina north to Randolph County, West Virginia.

Distribution in Virginia.—Probably occurs at higher elevations in all the counties west of the Blue Ridge, although specimens have been taken only in Grayson and Highland Counties. See figure 76.

Habitat.—Most common in thick spruce, fir and hemlock forests, but also occurs sparingly in mixed deciduous forests.

Remarks.—It is known in the mountain sections by several names, the most common of which are: fairy-diddle, mountain boomer, pine squirrel, and red squirrel.

Tamiasciurus hudsonicus loquax (Bangs)

Type Locality.—Liberty Hill, New London County, Connecticut.

Distinguishing Characteristics. Distinguished from *Tamiasciurus h abieticola* by brighter and more rusty coloration and from other Virginia squirrels by small size and reddish coloration. It is easily distinguished from the fox squirrel by its much smaller size, being only about one-third as large.

Measurements.—"Average measurements of twenty-eight adults from western New York are as follows: Total length, 310 mm.; tail, 120.4 mm.; hind foot, 46 mm." (Hamilton 1943.)

General Distribution.—Southeastern Ontario and southern Maine south to eastern Virginia and west through Ohio and Indiana to Wisconsin.

Distribution in Virginia.—The northeastern portion of the State, probably including the Blue Ridge Mountains; south at least to Buckingham and Henrico Counties. Abundant in the vicinity of Washington. See figure 76.

Habitat.—Forested and rural areas, building its nests both in trees and in houses.

Sciurus carolinensis

Gray Squirrel

General Description.—A large squirrel with long bushy tail and ears without tufts. Upper parts grayish or yellowish brown, palest in winter; underparts white; tail with hairs brown at base, blackish near middle, and tipped with gray. Distinguished from *Sciurus niger neglectus* by its smaller size and paler coloration, and from all other Virginia squirrels by the uniform grayish upper parts including feet, nose, and ears.

Distribution in Virginia.—State-wide.

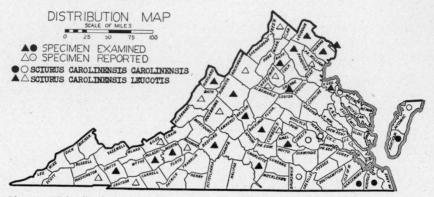

Fig. 77.—Distribution of the gray squirrels, *Sciurus carolinensis carolinensis* and *Sciurus carolinensis leucotis*, in Virginia.

Subspecies in Virginia

Sciurus carolinensis carolinensis Gmelin

Type Locality.—"Carolina."

Distinguishing Characteristics.—Distinguished from *Sciurus c. leucotis* by smaller size and paler coloration.

Measurements.—"Average measurements of ten adults from north Florida and Georgia are: Total length, 439 mm.; tail, 201 mm.; hind foot, 60.5 mm." (Hamilton 1943.)

General Distribution.—Southeastern United States, except in the coastal region of Louisiana, from Delaware to central Florida, and west around the mountains to West Virginia, central Ohio, Illinois, Missouri, and Oklahoma.

Distribution in Virginia.—Probably occurs only in the Coastal Plain province of eastern Virginia. See figure 77.

Habitat.—Forests and rural districts.

Sciurus carolinensis leucotis Gapper

Type Locality.—Region between York (i. e., Toronto) and Lake Simcoe, Ontario.

Distinguishing Characteristics.—Similar to *Sciurus c. carolinensis,* but larger and brighter. Winter and summer pelages distinctly different, the back being bright olive brown in summer and silvery with a brownish dorsal band in winter.

Measurements.—Twelve adults from Montgomery County, Virginia, average: Total length, 474.6 mm. (445-550 mm.); tail vertebrae, 204.4 mm. (210-233 mm.); hind foot, 65.2 mm. (60-68 mm.).

General Distribution.—Northeastern United States and southeastern Canada from New Brunswick and southern Ontario south along the Atlantic Coast to New York and in the Appalachian Mountains to North Carolina; west through the Great Lakes States to eastern Minnesota.

Distribution in Virginia.—Range not definitely determined, but thought to include all the State except the Coastal Plain. Fairly typical *leucotis* occurs in the higher mountains, but the identity of the subspecies occurring in the lower elevations of the Piedmont is open to question. See figure 77.

Habitat.—Forests, both coniferous and deciduous, border lands, towns, and parks.

Sciurus niger

Fox Squirrel

General Description.—Size large (more than 550 mm.); ears relatively short, fur long and coarse; coloration variable, including gray, buff, rusty, and blackish phases; underparts may be white or similar to the coloration of the upper parts; coloration of upper parts generally uniform throughout, not showing a darkened median band down the back. Distinguished from other Virginia squirrels by larger size and heavier proportions.

Distribution in Virginia.—Occurs throughout the State but is rare and localized in most sections.

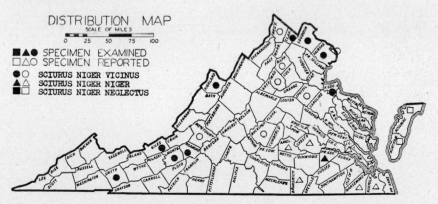

Fig. 78.—Distribution of the fox squirrels, *Sciurus niger niger, Sciurus niger neg-lectus,* and *Sciurus niger vicinus,* in Virginia.

Subspecies in Virginia

Sciurus niger niger Linnaeus

Type Locality.—Probably southern South Carolina.

Distinguishing Characteristics.—Size large (624 mm.), the largest of any squirrel occurring in Virginia. Coloration is variable, and there are three well-defined color phases as well as many intermediates. The gray phase is grayish above, including tail, and white below; the buff phase is buffy or reddish buff throughout, but darkest on back; the black phase is dark brown, rusty, or black throughout. The ears and nose are white in all phases, and the top of the head is always blackish. The feet are generally white but may be buffy or even blackish. Distinguished from *vicinus* by larger size and white ears and nose.

Measurements.—"Measurements of 14 Georgia and Florida adults average: Total length, 624 mm.; tail, 308.5 mm.; hind foot, 84.3 mm." (Hamilton 1943.)

General Distribution.—The southeastern United States from southern Virginia south to northern Florida and west to Alabama.

Distribution in Virginia.—Recorded on the basis of a single specimen from Prince George County. Fifty years ago it was common throughout southeast Virginia, but we have recent reports only from Chesterfield and Prince George Counties, and even there it is considered rare. See figure 78.

Habitat.—The fox squirrel may be found in varying woodland habitats, but apparently prefers upland pine forests.

Sciurus niger neglectus (Gray)

Type Locality.—Wilmington, Newcastle County, Delaware.

Distinguishing Characteristics.—Somewhat smaller than *S. n. niger;* back and tail grizzled and with a steel blue cast; belly, nose, ears, and feet white. Melanistic phases occur in which belly or back or both may be black. Easily confused with the gray squirrel, *S. c. carolinensis,* but is larger, the ears shorter, the fur longer, coarser, and more grizzled in appearance, and lacking the reddish flank stripe seen in the smaller animal.

Measurements.—"Ten adult males from Dorchester County, Md., average: Total length, 591 mm.; tail, 284 mm.; hind foot, 75 mm." (Poole 1944.)

General Distribution.—Formerly occurred along the Atlantic Coast from Virginia to western Connecticut, but now extinct excepting the eastern shore region of Delaware, Maryland and Virginia.

Distribution in Virginia.—Accomac and Northampton Counties, where its occurrence is based upon unpublished reports by Oberholser (field notes, 1895) and Llewellyn (field notes, 1944) which seem authentic. No specimens have been collected. See figure 78.

Habitat.—Old-growth loblolly pine forests are preferred, but it is also found in swamps where white oak and gum are the predominant trees.

Remarks.—Within its limited range this rare squirrel is known variously as "gray," "big gray," "cat," or "stump-eared" squirrel, while the much smaller gray squirrel, *S. c. carolinensis,* is known in some sections as "fox" squirrel!

Sciurus niger vicinus Bangs

Type Locality.—White Sulphur Springs, Greenbrier County, West Virginia.

Distinguishing Characteristics.—Somewhat smaller than typical *niger* and coloration less variable. Body generally buffy brown above and white below, tail grayish white above and rufous below, feet and ears rusty, and top of head blackish. Individual specimens show varying amounts of cinnamon or cream color on the belly and rusty in the tail. Varying degrees of white on the nose, ears, and feet may indicate a trend toward *niger.*

Measurements.—Three specimens from western Virginia average: Total length, 578 mm. (545-618 mm.); tail vertebrae, 279 mm. (265-302 mm.); hind foot, 75 mm. (72-77 mm.).

General Distribution.—Formerly occurred in the Appalachian Highlands from western North Carolina and Virginia north to central or northern New York, but now limited to western Virginia, eastern West Virginia, western Maryland, and south central Pennsylvania.

Distribution in Virginia.—All of the State west and north of Amelia County, but nowhere common. See figure 78.

Habitat. Open deciduous woodlands, woods borders, and orchards.

Glaucomys volans volans (Linnaeus)
Southern Flying Squirrel

Type Locality.—Virginia.

Distinguishing Characteristics.—A small squirrel characterized by a loose fold of skin extending along the sides between the fore and rear legs, extremely soft, dense and velvety fur, large prominent black eyes, and a broad flattened, well-furred tail. The color of the upper parts varies considerably with the season and with the age of the animal from grayish brown in the young to reddish brown and pinkish cinnamon in the adult. Underparts are white to creamy white and a dark chocolate brown streak extends along the side at the edge of the flying membrane; hairs of belly are snowy white from base to tip. Tail grayish above and cinnamon below; forefeet whitish; hind feet brown, except for whitish toes. Distinguished from *Glaucomys sabrinus* by much smaller size and pure white belly hairs.

Measurements.—Twenty-five adults from Virginia average: Total length, 228.4 mm. (213-245 mm.); tail vertebrae, 101 mm. (90-115 mm.); hind foot, 31 mm. (29-33 mm.).

General Distribution.—Northeastern United States and southern Ontario, from southern New Hampshire and central Minnesota south to northeastern Oklahoma and North Carolina, and in the mountains to northern Georgia.

Fig. 79.—Distribution of the southern flying squirrel, *Glaucomys volans volans,* in Virginia.

Distribution in Virginia.—State-wide. Common from sea level to the tops of the highest mountains wherever suitable forests occur. See figure 79.

Habitat.—Forests, apparently showing little preference for type, but perhaps favoring evergreens a little more than others. We have taken it in Virginia in spruce, fir, pine, oak, hickory, chestnut, beech, and gum forests in about equal numbers. It oftens invades the attics of houses and bird nesting boxes to build its own nest.

Remarks,—A large series of Virginia specimens, including a number from Amelia and Brunswick Counties, were compared with topotypical examples of *Glaucomys v. saturatus* from Alabama and all proved to be clearly referable to *volans*. Virginia specimens are indistinguishable from specimens from Michigan and Pennsylvania.

Glaucomys sabrinus fuscus Miller
Northern Flying Squirrel

Type Locality.—Cranberry Glades, Pocahontas County, West Virginia.

Distinguishing Characteristics.—A medium-sized squirrel similar in form and appearance to *Glaucomys volans* but differing in the following respects: larger and tail noticeably wider, longer, thicker, and heavier; all over coloration darker; basal two-thirds of belly hairs dark gray and tipped with cinnamon or buff, giving a grayish cinnamon cast to the belly.

Measurements.—Two adults from Mt. Mitchell, North Carolina, average: Total length, 290 mm.; tail vertebrae, 136 mm.; hind foot, 40 mm.

General Distribution.—Apparently restricted to the higher portions of the southern Appalachian Highlands in West Virginia, North Carolina, and Tennessee. It has not been taken below 3300 feet elevation.

Distribution in Virginia.—Not recorded, but probably once occurred in western Virginia at higher elevations and should still be sought in areas where spruce and fir have survived. Such areas may be found in Grayson, Smyth, Tazewell, and Highland Counties.

Habitat.—Apparently restricted to areas in which spruce and fir abound, and may be found either in pure stands of the evergreens or in mixed forests of spruce, beech, maple, and birch.

Courtesy Fish and Wildlife Service

Fig. 80.—Beaver pond with dam in foreground and lodge at right center.

Family **Castoridae**

Castor canadensis

Beaver

General Description.—Size large (1030 mm.); body heavily built; legs short; tail horizontally flattened and scaly; hind feet webbed; ears short and rounded; pelage composed of long glossy guard hairs and soft short underfur. Color above, dark rich brown; underparts lighter; incisors orange. The large size, "paddle tail," and rich, soft fur make it impossible to mistake the beaver for any other American mammal.

Distribution in Virginia.—Formerly the whole State; now limited to areas where it has been restocked.

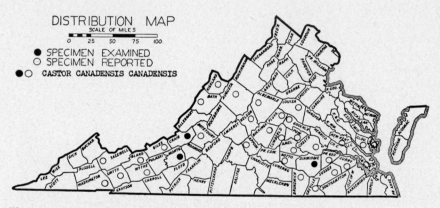

Fig. 81.—Present distribution of the beaver, *Castor canadensis canadensis,* in Virginia.

Subspecies in Virginia

Castor canadensis canadensis Kuhl

Type Locality.—Hudson Bay.

Distinguishing Characteristics.—Distinguished from *carolinensis* by smaller size, narrower tail, and darker coloration.

Measurements.—Nine adults from the Allegheny National Forest, Pennsylvania, average: Total length, 1031 mm. (970-1090 mm.); tail vertebrae, 358 mm. (260-440 mm.); greatest width of tail, 129 mm. (112-150 mm.); hind foot, 169 mm. (156-183 mm.); weight, 40 lbs. (27-48 lbs.). One is said to have been trapped in the James River, Virginia, about 1901, which weighed 67 lbs.

General Distribution.—Formerly occurred in the eastern United States east of the Mississippi River from Maine to Virginia and over most of forested Canada, except the Pacific slope, Newfoundland, and the area east of the St. Lawrence River, where other subspecies occur. It was exterminated and then re-introduced in much of its range in the United States.

Distribution in Virginia.—Formerly probably all of the State except the Dan and upper Roanoke River watersheds. Probably the last native beaver of this subspecies in Virginia were killed in Dinwiddie County in 1911. See figure 82. Since then it has been reestablished at numerous localities in the Piedmont and Mountain sections and appears to be doing well. See figure 81.

Habitat.—Wooded stream courses.

Castor canadensis carolinensis Rhoads

Type Locality.—Dan River, near Danbury, Stokes County, North Carolina.

Distinguishing Characteristics.—Similar to *C. c. canadensis,* but larger, tail relatively broader, and coloration brighter—more reddish.

Measurements.—An adult from Montgomery County, Alabama, measured: "Total length, 1035 mm.; length of tail, 290 mm.; greatest breadth of tail, 163 mm.; hind foot, 170 mm." (A. H. Howell 1921.) Adults weigh 35-65 pounds.

General Distribution.—Southeastern United States from southern Virginia and Tennessee south to east Texas and northern Florida. Now extinct in much of this area.

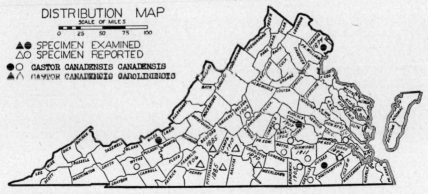

Fig. 82.—Former distribution of the beavers, *Castor canadensis canadensis* and *Castor canadensis carolinensis,* in Virginia. Figures indicate approximate dates of extinction.

Distribution in Virginia.—Limits of range are not known, but it certainly inhabited the watersheds of the Dan and upper Roanoke Rivers, north probably to Bedford and Charlotte Counties. The last known Virginia colony disappeared from Falling River in Campbell County about 1910. See figure 82. All beavers restocked in Virginia have been of the northern variety, *canadensis.*

Habitat.—Forested streams.

Family **Cricetidae**

Reithrodontomys humulis

Harvest Mouse

General Description.—Size small (125 mm.); tail about half of total length; upper parts cinnamon brown to gray brown; underparts grayish white; tail grayish black above and whitish below; feet white. The cinnamon hues of the adult replaced by blackish gray in the immature. Easily distinguished from most other Virginia mice by small size, and from the superficially similar house mouse by conspicuously grooved upper incisors.

Distribution in Virginia.—State-wide.

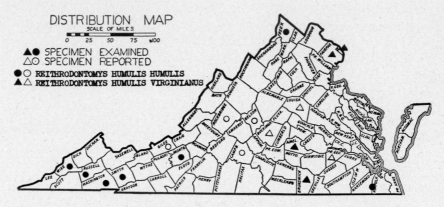

Fig. 83.—Distribution of the harvest mice, *Reithrodontomys humulis humulis* and *Reithrodontomys humulis virginianus,* in Virginia.

Subspecies in Virginia

Reithrodontomys humulis humulis   (Audubon and Bachman)

Type Locality.—Charleston, Charleston County, South Carolina.

Distinguishing Characteristics.—Upper parts dark cinnamon brown, darkest on the back, and brightest on the shoulders and flanks; cheeks bright cinnamon; underparts grayish white to light cinnamon. Distinguished from *Reithrodontomys humulis virginianus* by reddish rather than grayish coloration.

Measurements.—Twenty adults from Blacksburg, Montgomery County, Virginia, average: Total length, 126.4 mm. (117-152 mm.); tail vertebrae, 59.0 mm. (51-73 mm.); hind foot, 15.9 mm. (15-17 mm.).

General Distribution.—From near the Mississippi River in eastern Louisiana eastward and northward through the Gulf and South Atlantic States to extreme southeastern Virginia, and through the Appalachian Mountains to western Virginia and southern Ohio.

Distribution in Virginia.—The Dismal Swamp and all of western Virginia west of the central Piedmont, the intervening territory occupied by the subspecies *virginianus*. See figure 83.

Habitat.—Old fields, pastures and marshes.

Reithrodontomys humulis virginianus Howell

Type Locality.—Amelia Court House, Amelia County, Virginia.

Distinguishing Characteristics.—Similar to *humulis*, but smaller and grayer; distinguished from the house mouse, which it resembles, by its grooved upper incisors.

Measurements.—"Averages and extremes of four young adults from Amelia, Virginia: Total length, 122 mm. (116-125 mm.); tail vertebrae, 53 mm. (47-57 mm.); hind foot, 16.0 mm. (15.5-17.0 mm.)" (Hooper 1943).

General Distribution.—Central Virginia and southern Maryland from southern Brunswick County, Virginia, north to Takoma Park, Maryland.

Distribution in Virginia.—Upper Coastal Plain and Piedmont Provinces of central Virginia from southern Brunswick County north to Arlington County. See figure 83.

Habitat.—Old fields, wet meadows and bogs.

Peromyscus maniculatus nubiterrae Rhoads
Deer Mouse

Type Locality.—Summit of Roan Mountain, Mitchell County, North Carolina. Altitude, 6,370 feet.

Distinguishing Characteristics.—Size medium (179 mm.); tail more than half the total length, with conspicuous pencil of hairs at tip; eyes large; color of sides and face, russet brown, and back somewhat darker; belly white; line of demarcation on sides sharp; tail sharply bicolor, grayish brown above, white beneath; feet white. The brown of adults replaced by gray in the immature. Typical specimens can be distinguished from *Peromyscus leucopus* by the much longer and sharply bicolor penicillate tail, and duller coloration. Other specimens are confusingly similar to *leucopus* and may be distinguished with certainty only by examination of the skull.

Measurements.—Twenty-five adults from Whitetop Mountain, Smyth and Grayson Counties, Virginia, taken at elevations above 5,000 feet, average: Total length, 178.8 mm. (166-200 mm.); tail vertebrae, 90.6 mm. (77-102 mm.); hind foot, 20.4 mm. (20-22.5 mm.).

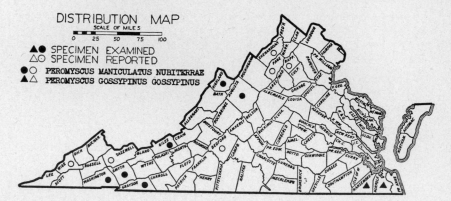

Fig. 84.—Distribution of the deer mouse, *Peromyscus maniculatus nubiterrae,* and the cotton mouse, *Peromyscus gossypinus gossypinus,* in Virginia.

General Distribution.—At high elevations in the Appalachian Highlands from western New York south to northern Georgia.

Distribution in Virginia.—Found throughout the mountains at elevations usually above 2500 feet. Abundant. See figure 84.

Habitat.—Woodlands; most abundant among mossy boulders and logs in moist spruce and birch forests on the higher mountains; sometimes invades houses. It is frequently found associated with *Peromyscus leucopus* in dryer, warmer habitats.

Remarks.—The short-tailed western subspecies, *bairdii,* should be sought for in the extreme southwestern counties, for it has been taken in Tennessee within thirty miles of Lee County, Virginia.

Peromyscus leucopus
White-footed Mouse

General Description.—Size medium (170 mm.); tail usually less than half the total length; upper parts grayish brown to dull orange brown, darkest on the back; underparts white; line of demarcation along sides sharp; tail brownish black above, white to dusky beneath; feet white. The brown of adults replaced by gray in young individuals.

Distribution in Virginia.—State-wide, except on the summits of the highest mountains.

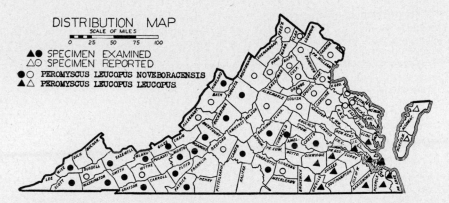

Fig. 85.—Distribution of the white-footed mice *Peromyscus leucopus leucopus* and *Peromyscus leucopus noveboracensis,* in Virginia.

Subspecies in Virginia

Peromyscus leucopus leucopus   (Rafinesque)

Type Locality.—Barrens of western Kentucky, probably near the mouth of the Ohio River.

Distinguishing Characteristics. —Distinguished from *Peromyscus l. noveboracensis* by smaller size and darker coloration, and from *Peromyscus gossypinus* by smaller size and slighter build.

Measurements.—Eight adults from Virginia Beach, Princess Anne County, Virginia average: Total length, 168.3 mm. (152-185 mm.); tail vertebrae, 73.3 mm. (65-83 mm.); hind foot, 20.8 mm. (20-21 mm.).

General Distribution.—From southeastern Virginia south to Georgia; west to eastern Oklahoma; north in the Mississippi Valley to western Kentucky.

Distribution in Virginia.—Southeastern section as far west and north as Brunswick, Dinwiddie, Prince George, Gloucester, and Accomac Counties. See figure 85.

Habitat.—Woods, thickets, old fields, cane brakes and marshes.

Remarks.—Although A. H. Howell and W. H. Osgood identified specimens from as far inland as Dinwiddie and Gloucester Counties as *leucopus,* we suspect that further collecting will show that typical *leucopus* does not occur north and west of Dismal Swamp.

Peromyscus leucopus noveboracensis   (Fischer)

Type Locality.—New York.

Distinguishing Characteristics.—Slightly larger and paler than *leucopus* but otherwise similar. Distinguished from *Peromyscus maniculatus nubiterrae,* with which it is easily confused, by shorter tail, brighter coloration, and cranial details.

Measurements.—Ten adults from northwestern Highland County, Virginia, average: Total length, 170.7 mm. (160-184 mm.); tail vertebrae, 77.1 mm. (65-87 mm.); hind foot, 20.6 mm. (20-22 mm.).

General Distribution.—Northern United States and southern Canada, north to central Minnesota and southern Maine; south to western North Carolina and central Missouri and west to eastern Nebraska.

Distribution in Virginia.—The whole State, west and north of Dinwiddie, Prince George and Gloucester Counties. See figure 85.

Habitat.—Abundant everywhere; woods, thickets, pastures, cultivated fields, marshes, and buildings. It usually shuns the cool, damp habitats preferred by *Peromyscus m. nubiterrae.*

Remarks.—The white-footed mouse is undoubtedly the most abundant and most frequently encountered of all the wild mammals in Virginia. It is known variously as white-footed mouse, deer mouse, and wood mouse.

Peromyscus gossypinus gossypinus (LeConte)
Cotton Mouse

Type Locality.—Georgia; probably near Riceboro, Liberty County.

Distinguishing Characteristics.—Size medium to large (178 mm.); tail less than half the total length and indistinctly bicolored; hind foot large. Upper parts bright cinnamon rufous to deep russet, sprinkled with black and darker along the back; underparts dirty white; feet white; tail blackish brown above, dull white below. Distinguished from *Peromyscus leucopus* by darker coloration, stockier build, shorter tail, and larger hind foot.

Measurements.—Average of ten adults from Dismal Swamp, Virginia: Total length, 178 mm. (170-188 mm.); tail vertebrae, 79 mm. (70-84 mm.); hind foot 23.1 mm. (22-24 mm.).

General Distribution.—Lowlands of the southeastern United States from southeastern Virginia south to northern Florida and west to central Louisiana.

Distribution in Virginia.—Known only from the Dismal Swamp; has been taken as far north as Suffolk at the northern edge of the swamp.

Habitat.—A. K. Fisher found them to be numerous in or near cane in the Dismal Swamp and trapped one in a building there (field notes, 1895).

Remarks.—The Mississippi Valley subspecies, *megacephalus,* should be sought in extreme southwestern Virginia, for it has been taken in Tennessee at a point only about twenty-five miles from Lee County, Virginia.

Peromyscus nuttalli

Golden Mouse

General Description.—A medium-sized mouse with unusually soft, thick fur. Color above, bright orange or tawny ochraceous; sides paler; underparts creamy white with no sharp line of demarcation along the sides; ears ochraceous; feet creamy white; tail, gray brown above, white below. Young similar to adults but much paler. Distinguished from *Peromyscus leucopus* and *Peromyscus gossypinus* by much smaller eyes, softer, thicker fur, creamy rather than white coloration of the belly, and by the absence of a sharp line of demarcation along the sides.

Distribution in Virginia.—The southern third of the State, north to Amelia, Campbell, and Montgomery Counties.

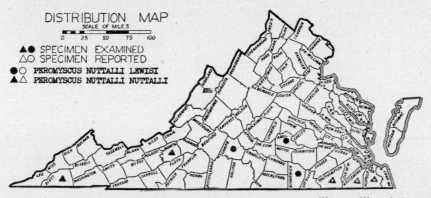

Fig. 86.—Distribution of the golden mice, *Peromyscus nuttalli nuttalli* and *Peromyscus nuttalli lewisi*, in Virginia.

Subspecies in Virginia

Peromyscus nuttalli nuttalli (Harlan)

Type Locality.—Norfolk, Norfolk County, Virginia.

Distinguishing Characteristics.—Distinguished from *Peromyscus n. lewisi* by the darker, more burnished coloration of the back.

Measurements.—Average of 10 adults from the Dismal Swamp, Virginia (Osgood 1909): Total length, 181 mm. (170-190 mm.); tail vertebrae, 85 mm. (80-93 mm.); hind foot, 19.7 mm. (19-20 mm.).

General Distribution.—From southeastern Virginia and northeastern North Carolina west through the Great Smoky Mountains to southwestern Virginia and eastern Kentucky.

Distribution in Virginia.—Extreme southeastern Virginia in the vicinity of the Dismal Swamp and all of southwestern Virginia as far north as Montgomery County, the region between these two localities being inhabited by the subspecies *lewisi;* uncommon. See figure 86.

Habitat.—Woods and thickets, often in moist situations, and usually associated with honeysuckle (*Lonicera japonica*). In the Dismal Swamp, Fisher found it most commonly at the edges of cane brakes (field notes, 1895).

Remarks.—It seems likely that *Peromyscus n. aureolus* of the southeastern United States will prove to be synonymous with *nuttalli* when more specimens have been collected. In such a case, the range of *nuttalli* would then include all of the southeastern United States from southeastern and southwestern Virginia, southern Illinois and southern Missouri, south to eastern Texas and central Florida.

Peromyscus nuttalli lewisi   Howell

Type Locality.—Amelia Court House, Amelia County, Virginia.

Distinguishing Characteristics.—Similar to *Peromyscus n. nuttalli* but much paler and lacking to a large extent the burnished appearance of the back. It bears little resemblance to *Peromyscus leucopus* and may be easily distinguished by the same characteristics which serve to separate *nuttalli* from that species.

Measurements.—Average of six adults from the type locality, Amelia, Virginia: Total length, 172.2 mm. (166-177 mm.); tail vertebrae, 80.2 mm. (77-84 mm.); hind foot, 19.5 mm. (19-20.5 mm.).

General Distribution.—At present, known only from south central Virginia, from Campbell and Amelia Counties south to Brunswick County; common. See figure 86.

Habitat.—Woods and thickets, often in moist situations, and usually associated with honeysuckle (*Lonicera japonica*).

Oryzomys palustris palustris   (Harlan)

Rice Rat

Type Locality.—Near Salem, Salem County, New Jersey.

Distinguishing Characteristics.—Form rat-like; tail nearly half the total length; fur long and coarse. Upper parts grizzled or buffy brown, darker along the middle of the back; underparts grayish white; feet whitish; tail scaly and sparsely haired, brownish above and whitish below. Young grayer than adults. Distinguished from the young Norway rat, which it superficially resembles, by having two rather than three longitudinal rows of tubercles on the upper molars.

Measurements.—"Average measurements of 7 adults from Chincoteague, (Accomac County) Virginia, are: Total length, 252 mm.; tail, 121 mm.; hind foot, 30 mm." (Hamilton 1943).

General Distribution.—In the Coastal Plain and lower Piedmont from southern New Jersey south to northern Florida, west to eastern Mississippi, and north in the Mississippi Valley to southern Illinois and central Kentucky.

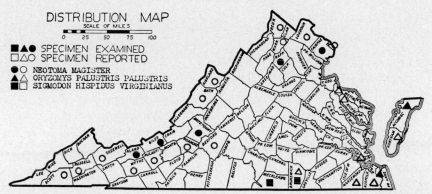

DISTRIBUTION MAP
SCALE OF MILES
0   25   50   75   100

■▲● SPECIMEN EXAMINED
□△○ SPECIMEN REPORTED
●○ NEOTOMA MAGISTER
▲△ ORYZOMYS PALUSTRIS PALUSTRIS
■□ SIGMODON HISPIDUS VIRGINIANUS

Fig. 87.—Distribution of the wood rat, *Neotoma magister;* the rice rat, *Oryzomys palustris palustris,* and the cotton rat, *Sigmodon hispidus virginianus,* in Virginia.

Distribution in Virginia.—Coastal Plain and Piedmont, west to Brunswick and Westmoreland Counties; abundant. It should also be sought in the extreme southwestern counties, for it has been taken at nearby points in Tennessee. See figure 87.

Habitat.—Marshes, watercourses, wet meadows, cane brakes, swamps, and sometimes dry fields.

Sigmodon hispidus virginianus Gardner
Cotton Rat

Type Locality.—Triplet, Brunswick County, Virginia.

Distinguishing Characteristics.—A medium-sized rat-like rodent with comparatively short tail and rather coarse fur. Upper parts buffy brown with many of the hairs black tipped, giving the appearance of streaking; underparts grayish white; line of demarcation on sides not sharp; feet buffy, streaked with black and white; tail black above and brownish white below. Young similar to adults. The cotton rat cannot be confused with any other Virginia mammal.

Measurements.—Three adults from Brunswick County, Virginia, average: Total length, 239 mm. (225-266 mm.); tail vertebrae, 88 mm. (81-100 mm.); hind foot, 31.3 mm. (30-33 mm.).

General Distribution.—Southern Virginia.

Distribution in Virginia.—Known only from southern Brunswick and Mecklenburg Counties where it is locally common. Another subspecies, *Sigmodon hispidus hispidus,* should be found in the southwestern counties of Lee, Scott and Washington. See figure 87.

Habitat.—Dense matted grasses and sedges, sometimes in rather damp situations, but often in dry fallow fields.

Neotoma magister Baird
Wood Rat

Type Locality.—Carlisle, Cumberland County, or Harrisburg, Dauphin County, Pennsylvania.

Distinguishing Characteristics.—A large rat-like rodent with buffy gray back, buffy or reddish brown sides, white belly and feet, gray ears, and bi-colored tail, gray above and white below. Young similar to adult but grayer. It can be distinguished from the somewhat similar Norway rat by its grayish rather than brownish coloration, its hairy bicolor rather than scaly mono-color tail, its much longer whiskers, and its longer ears. From the black rats it may be distinguished by its much shorter tail.

Measurements.—Four adults from western Virginia average: Total length, 402 mm. (378-425 mm.); tail vertebrae, 185 mm. (180-195 mm.); hind foot, 43 mm. (40-45 mm.).

General Distribution.—The Appalachian Highlands from western Connecticut and southern New York south through western Virginia and eastern Tennessee to northern Alabama; west to central Kentucky, southern Indiana, southern Ohio and southwestern Pennsylvania.

Distribution in Virginia.—Common from the Blue Ridge westward wherever suitable habitat occurs; east of the Blue Ridge along cliffs and bluffs of river valleys as far east as Arlington County. See figure 87.

Habitat.—Cliffs, rock slides, and caves

Synaptomys cooperi
Lemming Mouse

General Description.—Size medium (126 mm.); tail short; upper incisors longitudinally grooved; fur coarse. Upper parts mixed black, gray, and yellowish brown, giving a grizzled cinnamon brown appearance; underparts grayish white or grayish cream; no sharp line of demarcation on sides; tail grayish black, not sharply bicolor; feet brownish black. Distinguished from *Microtus* and all other Virginia mice by the combination of grooved incisors and extremely short tail.

Distribution in Virginia.—Common in the mountains and upper Piedmont but absent from the lowlands except in the Dismal Swamp.

Subspecies in Virginia

Synaptomys cooperi helaletes Merriam

Type Locality.—Lake Drummond, Dismal Swamp, Norfolk County, Virginia.

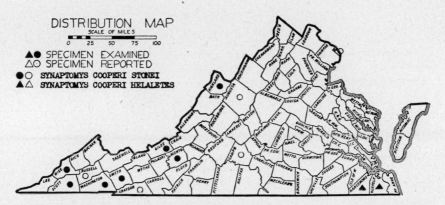

Fig. 88.—Distribution of the lemming mice, *Synaptomys cooperi helaletes* and *Synaptomys cooperi stonei,* in Virginia.

Distinguishing Characteristics.—Similar to *stonei* but slightly brighter and with a large, heavy skull and broad, short rostrum.

Measurements.—Average of nine adults from the Dismal Swamp: Total length, 129 mm.; tail vertebrae, 21.4 mm.; hind foot, 20 mm. (A. B. Howell, 1927).

General Distribution.—Extreme southeastern Virginia and northeastern North Carolina.

Distribution in Virginia.—Dismal Swamp See figure 88.

Habitat.—Cane brakes, sphagnum bogs, and occasionally dry grassland.

Synaptomys cooperi stonei Rhoads

Type Locality.—Mays Landing, Atlantic County, New Jersey.

Distinguishing Characteristics.—Distinguished from *helaletes* by duller coloration, smaller size, and cranial details.

Measurements.—Fourteen adults from western Virginia average: Total length, 125.9 mm. (119-135 mm.); tail vertebrae, 20.6 mm. (17-25 mm.); hind foot, 19.1 mm. (18-20 mm.).

General Distribution.—Coastal Massachusetts and New Jersey, southwest and west to western North Carolina and southeastern Ohio.

Distribution in Virginia.—All of the western part of the State and east to Campbell and Arlington Counties. Common. See figure 88.

Habitat.—Sphagnum bogs, moist meadows, marsh borders, and at higher altitudes dry fields and thickets.

Clethrionomys gapperi

Red-backed Mouse

General Description.—Size medium (148 mm.); tail less than one-third of total length. Upper parts rusty red in a wide dorsal band, grayish buff on sides and face; underparts grayish white; feet gray; tail blackish above, paler below. A darker color phase is frequently encountered. Distinguished from other Virginia mice by the combination of short tail and red dorsal band (the pine mouse also has a reddish back, but the red is not restricted to a band on the back and extends onto the sides as well).

Distribution in Virginia.—All counties west of the Piedmont.

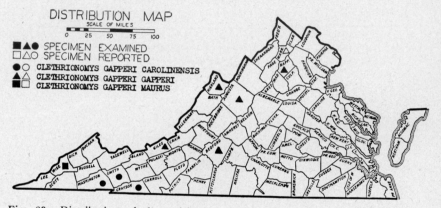

Fig. 89.—Distribution of the red-backed mice, *Clethrionomys gapperi gapperi*, *Clethrionomys gapperi carolinensis*, and *Clethrionomys gapperi maurus*, in Virginia.

Subspecies in Virginia

Clethrionomys gapperi gapperi (Vigors).

Type Locality.—Between York and Lake Simcoe, Ontario, Canada.

Distinguishing Characteristics.—Set apart from *Clethrionomys g. carolinensis* and *Clethrionomys g. maurus* by smaller size and paler coloration.

Measurements.—Ten adults from Highland County, Virginia, average: Total length, 146.4 mm. (140-153 mm.); tail vertebrae, 43.4 mm. (41-46 mm.); hind foot, 19.3 mm. (18-20 mm.).

General Distribution.—From Massachusetts southward through the Appalachian Highlands to western Virginia and westward across New York and Michigan to the Rocky Mountains in Canada.

Distribution in Virginia.—The mountainous portion of the State south to Giles and Bedford Counties. This is one of the most abundant mice on the cooler forested slopes of our mountains. See figure 89.

Habitat.—Abundant among mossy rocks and rotting logs in cool, damp, forested situations.

Clethrionomys gapperi carolinensis (Merriam)

Type Locality.—Roan Mountain, Mitchell County, North Carolina. Altitude, 6,000 feet.

Distinguishing Characteristics.—Similar to *gapperi* but much darker and brighter and slightly larger. There are two color phases, one dark and blackish and the other lighter and buffy.

Measurements.—Fifteen adults from Whitetop Mountain, Smyth and Grayson Counties, Virginia, average: Total length, 148.7 mm. (140-155 mm.); tail vertebrae, 42.6 mm. (38-50 mm.); hind foot, 19.9 mm. (19-21 mm.).

General Distribution.—The mountains of North Carolina, Tennessee, and southwest Virginia.

Distribution in Virginia.—The counties west of New River, except those bordering Kentucky. See figure 89.

Habitat.—Among mossy rocks and rotting logs in cool, damp, forested situations.

Clethrionomys gapperi maurus Kellogg

Type Locality.—Black Mountains, 4½ miles southeast of Lynch, altitude 4,100 feet, Harlan County, Kentucky.

Distinguishing Characteristics.—Similar to *C. g. carolinensis* but darker and more blackish. Slightly larger than *C. g. gapperi* and much darker.

Measurements.—"Average of 6 adult female topotypes, including type: Total length, 153.8 mm. (147-172); tail, 37.8 mm. (36-41); hind foot, 19.5 mm. (19-20)" (Kellogg 1939).

General Distribution.—Apparently confined to the Cumberland Mountains along the Kentucky-Virginia state line.

Distribution in Virginia.—Has been taken only in Big Stone Gap, Wise County. See figure 89.

Habitat.—Cool, damp, shaded slopes; found among spruces on Black Mountain and among hemlocks in Big Stone Gap.

Remarks.—The Wise County specimens which we have seen do not seem to be distinct or distinguishable from specimens from Roan Mountain, the type locality of *C. g. carolinensis*. They are, however, quite different from Mountain Lake (Giles County) specimens which are typical *C. g. gapperi*.

Fig. 90.—Specimens of Mice from the Fish and Wildlife Service collection. Left, Meadow Mouse; right, Pine Mouse.

Microtus pennsylvanicus

Meadow Mouse

General Description.—Size medium (173 mm.); tail less than one-third of total length; fur long, overlaid with coarse hairs. Upper parts dull chestnut brown, bright yellowish chestnut, or blackish, darkest along middle of back; underparts grayish white or grayish cinnamon; feet grayish brown; tail dusky above, paler below. Distinguished from the pine mouse by longer coarser fur and longer tail; from the red-backed mouse by larger size and absence of red dorsal band; and from the lemming mouse by longer tail and absence of grooved upper incisors.

Distribution in Virginia.—State-wide.

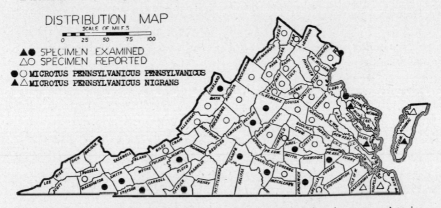

Fig. 91.—Distribution of the meadow mice, *Microtus pennsylvanicus pennsylvanicus* and *Microtus pennsylvanicus nigrans,* in Virginia.

Subspecies in Virginia

Microtus pennsylvanicus pennsylvanicus (Ord)

Type Locality.—Meadows below Philadelphia, Pennsylvania.

Distinguishing Characteristics.—Distinguished from *Microtus pennsylvanicus nigrans* by lighter, more yellowish coloration.

Measurements.—Thirty adults from Blacksburg, Montgomery County, Virginia, average: Total length, 173.9 mm. (160-190 mm.); tail vertebrae, 46.2 mm. (40-54 mm.); hind foot, 22.3 mm. (20-26 mm.).

General Distribution.—Eastern United States, south and west to South Carolina and Nebraska.

Distribution in Virginia.—Abundant over the whole State, except in the brackish and salt marshes of the Coastal Plain where the subspecies *nigrans* occurs. See figure 91.

Habitat.—Dry fields, thickets, bogs, wet meadows, and fresh water marshes.

Microtus pennsylvanicus nigrans **Rhoads**

Type Locality.—Currituck, Currituck County, North Carolina.

Distinguishing Characteristics.—Similar to *pennsylvanicus* but darker, the back almost black in some pelages.

Measurements.—Twelve adults from Chincoteague, Accomac County, Virginia, average: Total length, 171 mm.; tail vertebrae, 43.5 mm.; hind foot, 23 mm. (Hamilton 1943).

General Distribution.—Near the coast from southeastern Maryland south to northeastern North Carolina.

Distribution in Virginia.—The Coastal Plain, inland at least to Richmond County. See figure 91.

Habitat.—Brackish and salt marshes.

Microtus chrotorrhinus carolinensis Komarek
Yellow-nosed Vole

Type Locality.—Five miles north of Smokemont, Swain County, North Carolina. Altitude, 3,200 feet.

Distinguishing characteristics.—Similar in appearance to *Microtus pennsylvanicus* and distinguished from it by a deep orange rufous spot from the nose to the eye, and by a somewhat more orange coloration throughout.

Measurements.—Fifteen adults from Cranberry Glades, West Virginia, average: Total length, 154.4 mm. (150-169 mm.); tail vertebrae, 48.6 mm. (43-60 mm.); hind foot, 20.2 mm. (20-21 mm.).

General Distribution.—The southern Appalachian Highlands from North Carolina and Tennessee north to Randolph County, West Virginia.

Distribution in Virginia.—Not recorded. It has been taken in West Virginia at a point less than ten miles from Highland County, Virginia.

Habitat.—Found among mossy rocks and rotting logs, often near water, in cool, moist forests.

Pitymys pinetorum
Pine Mouse

General Description.—Size small (130 mm.); tail very short; ears small and hidden in fur; pelage short and soft; color bright, and pelage glossy. Upper parts bright russet brown to chestnut brown, becoming somewhat lighter on sides; underparts grayish buff; tail buffy brown above, lighter below; feet grayish brown. The red tones of the adult replaced by dark brown in the immature. Easily distinguished from other Virginia mice by the short tail and short, soft, almost mole-like fur.

Distribution in Virginia.—Common throughout the State.

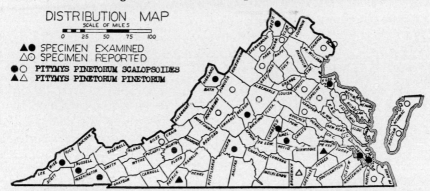

Fig. 92.—Distribution of the pine mice, *Pitymys pinetorum pinetorum* and *Pitymys pinetorum scalopsoides,* in Virginia.

Subspecies in Virginia

Pitymys pinetorum pinetorum (LeConte)

Type Locality.—Pine forests of Georgia, presumably near Riceboro, Liberty County.

Distinguishing Characteristics. Distinguished from *Pitymys p. scalopsoides* by smaller feet and brighter coloration.

Measurements.—Twenty-five adults from Patrick County, Virginia, average: Total length, 130.2 mm. (125-142 mm.); tail vertebrae, 23.2 mm. (20-27 mm.); hind foot, 16.6 mm. (15-18 mm.).

General Distribution.—From central Alabama northeast to southern Virginia.

Distribution in Virginia.—South central counties from Patrick to Prince George. Abundant. See figure 92.

Habitat.—Orchards, borders of cultivated fields, open woods and deserted fields; preferring loose sandy soil.

Remarks.—Remington Kellogg identified the specimens from Patrick County as *pinetorum,* and one specimen which we have examined from Prince George County is equally as bright. We have not seen specimens from Brunswick or Norfolk Counties, but suspect that they may prove to be *pinetorum.*

Pitymys pinetorum scalopsoides   (Audubon and Bachman)

Type Locality.—Long Island, New York.

Distinguishing Characteristics.—Similar to *pinetorum*, but duller and darker, the upper parts being dull brownish chestnut.

Measurements.—Three adults from Blacksburg, Montgomery County, Virginia, average: Total length, 126.3 mm. (125-128 mm.); tail vertebrae, 23.3 mm. (22-24 mm.); hind foot, 17.7 mm. (16-20 mm.).

General Distribution.—Northeastern United States from New Hampshire south and west to western North Carolina and Wisconsin.

Distribution in Virginia.—The whole State excepting the south central counties. Common. See figure 92.

Habitat.—Orchards, old fields, woods borders, and edges of cultivated fields, preferring loose sandy soils.

Remarks.—Specimens from the extreme southwestern counties have extremely dark and glossy fur and are not clearly referable to *scalopsoides*. They may be *auricularis,* the subspecies of the central United States.

Ondatra zibethica
Muskrat

General Description.—Size large (600 mm.); tail long and laterally compressed; hind feet large and toes only partially webbed; ears small and almost hidden in fur; pelage dense, the under fur soft and overlaid by long coarse guard hairs. Upper parts glossy chestnut brown, darkest on the head and back and lighter on the sides; underparts light brown; feet brown; tail blackish. Can be mistaken only for the beaver, from which it differs by much smaller size; laterally flattened, rather than dorsoventrally flattened, tail; and only partially webbed hind feet.

Distribution in Virginia.—State-wide.

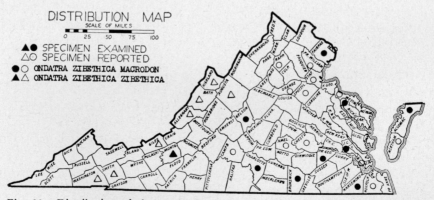

Fig. 93.—Distribution of the muskrats, *Ondatra zibethica zibethica* and *Ondatra zibethica macrodon,* in Virginia.

Subspecies in Virginia

Ondatra zibethica zibethica   (Linnaeus)

Type Locality.—Eastern Canada.

Distinguishing Characteristics.—Distinguished from *Ondatra z. macrodon* by smaller size and darker coloration.

Measurements.—Ten adults from Blacksburg, Montgomery County, Virginia, average: Total length, 585 mm. (549-705 mm.); tail vertebrae, 257 mm. (250-283 mm.); hind foot, 83 mm. (76-90 mm.).

General Distribution.—Southeastern Canada and eastern United States; from New Brunswick and western Ontario south to Arkansas and northern Georgia, except along the Atlantic seaboard south of Delaware Bay.

Distribution in Virginia.—All counties west of the Blue Ridge Mountains. Abundant. See figure 93.

Habitat.—Streams, marshes, swamps, and ponds.

Remarks.—Rarely occurs in the black phase which is so common in *Ondatra z. macrodon.*

Ondatra zibethica macrodon   (Merriam)

Type Locality.—Lake Drummond, Dismal Swamp, Virginia.

Distinguishing Characteristics.—Similar to *Ondatra z. zibethica*, but larger and pelage lighter and brighter. A black phase in which the entire upper parts are uniform brownish black is common in many marshes.

Measurements. "Average of four adults from the Dismal Swamp, Virginia: Total length, 620 mm.; tail vertebrae, 274 mm.; hind foot, 88 mm." (Hollister 1911).

General Distribution. Atlantic Coast region of the United States from Delaware to North Carolina; inland to Rappahannock County, Virginia, and Raleigh, North Carolina.

Distribution in Virginia.—All counties east of the Blue Ridge Mountains. Abundant. See figure 93.

Habitat.—Fresh and salt water marshes, ditches, lake shores, and swamps.

Family **Muridae**

Rattus rattus

Black Rat

General Description.—Similar to *Rattus norvegicus,* but distinguished from it and native rats by the long tail, which is more than half the total length. Coloration of upper parts varies from black to brown, and underparts may be gray, lemon, or white.

Distribution in Virginia.—Locally common in widely separated parts of the State; apparently completely lacking in the intervening territory.

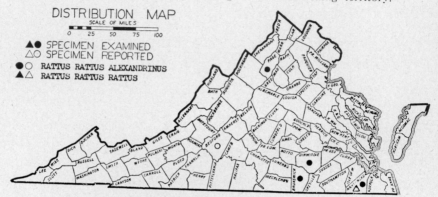

Fig. 94.—Distribution of the black rats, *Rattus rattus rattus* and *Rattus rattus alexandrinus,* in Virginia.

Subspecies in Virginia

Rattus rattus rattus   (Linnaeus)

Type Locality.—Upsala, Sweden.

Distinguishing Characteristics.—Upper parts black or blackish; underparts sooty; and tail more than half the total length. Distinguished from *Rattus r. alexandrinus* by dark coloration.

Measurements.—"Twelve adults from Alabama, Florida, Georgia, Massachusetts, New Hampshire, and Virginia average: Total length, 369 mm. (327-430 mm.); tail 193 mm. (160-220 mm.); hind foot, 35.5 mm. (33-39 mm.)." (Hamilton 1943.)

General Distribution.—Cosmopolitan; most common in the tropics. It cannot live in competition with the barbaric Norway rat and thus is often completely absent over wide areas. Native only to Europe.

Distribution in Virginia.—Only two records, both from the Dismal Swamp. Either very rare or totally extinct in Virginia today. See figure 94.

Habitat.—Woods, swamps, ships, and upper stories of buildings.

Rattus rattus alexandrinus   (Geoffroy)

Type Locality.—Alexandria, Egypt.

Distinguishing Characteristics.—Similar in form to *Rattus rattus rattus,* but paler and more like *Rattus norvegicus.* Upper parts grayish to reddish brown; underparts gray, lemon, or white.

Measurements.—Three adults from Brunswick and Dinwiddie Counties, Virginia, average: Total length, 394 mm. (375-406 mm.); tail vertebrae, 201 mm. (200-201 mm.); hind foot, 34 mm. (30-37 mm.).

General Distribution.—Introduced from Europe into all warm countries.

Distribution in Virginia.—Probably state-wide before the advent of the Norway rat; now known to occur only in Brunswick and Dinwiddie Counties, but may be expected anywhere in southeastern Virginia. See figure 94.

Habitat.—Forests and upper stories of buildings; often building its nests in trees.

Rattus norvegicus   (Berkenhout)

House Rat

Type Locality.—Norway.

Distinguishing Characteristics.—Size large (420 mm.); tail scaly and less than half of total length; pelage coarse; ears short. Upper parts dark brown streaked with black; underparts dirty white or grayish; feet brownish white; tail blackish. Coal black individuals are frequently encountered, and albinism is prevalent in some localities. Distinguished from *Rattus rattus* by shorter tail; from *Neotoma* by scaly tail and short ears; and from *Oryzomys* by much heavier tail, darker coloration, and "Roman nose." Three longitudinal rows of cusps on the molar teeth of *Rattus* distinguish it with certainty from the native rats which have only two rows.

Measurements.—Five adults from Virginia average: Total length, 417 mm. (400-440 mm.); tail vertebrae, 196 mm. (180-215 mm.); hind foot, 44 mm. (42-45 mm.).

General Distribution.—Cosmopolitan, but native only to Europe.

Distribution in Virginia.—Almost state-wide; however, J. B. Lewis reports that there are none in southeastern Brunswick County where *Rattus rattus alexandrinus* is common.

Habitat.—Buildings, sewers, garbage dumps, stream banks, and sometimes marshes and fields.

Mus musculus Linnaeus
House Mouse

Type Locality.—Upsala, Sweden.

Distinguishing Characteristics.—Size small (165 mm.); tail nearly half the total length. Upper parts buffy brown to grayish brown; underparts white, gray or brown, often with a buffy line along the flanks; tail blackish; feet, or at least the toes, white. Distinguished from *Reithrodontomys,* the only small, buffy brown, long-tailed native mouse, by the absence of grooved upper incisors.

Measurements.—Four adults from western Virginia average: Total length, 165.8 mm. (154-175 mm.); tail vertebrae, 77.5 mm. (74-81 mm.); hind foot, 18.5 mm. (17-20 mm.).

General Distribution.—Native to Europe, but introduced and established in most parts of North America.

Distribution in Virginia.—Abundant in all parts of the State.

Habitat.—Buildings, meadows, marshes, and cultivated fields.

Remarks.—The light-bellied variety, recognized by some authors as *Mus musculus brevirostris* Waterhouse, is most frequent in the southeastern counties, while the dark-bellied variety, referred to as *Mus musculus domesticus* Rutty, is most common in the rest of the State; both varieties, as well as intermediates, are frequently found together in the same locality.

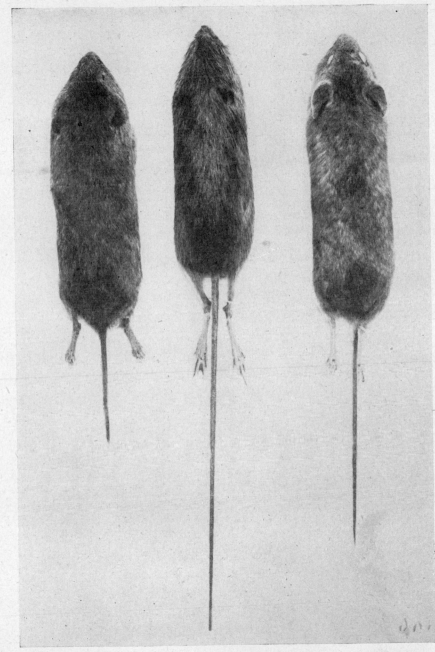

Courtesy Fish and Wildlife Service

Fig. 95.—Specimens of Mice from the Fish and Wildlife Service collection. Left to right: Red-backed Mouse, Meadow Jumping Mouse, and White-footed Mouse.

Family Zapodidae

Zapus hudsonius

Meadow Jumping Mouse

General Description.—Size medium (215 mm.); tail very long (130 mm.); hind legs greatly elongated; forelegs short; pelage rather coarse. Upper parts mixed orange yellow and black, the black most concentrated in a broad dorsal band extending from nose to tail, and the yellow most concentrated on the sides; the dorsal band sharply defined in some pelages, rather indistinct in others; underparts white, often suffused with the delicate orange yellow color of the sides; feet silvery white; tail blackish above, white below, not white tipped. Distinguished from *Napaeozapus* by having yellow rather than orange on the sides and by having the tail not white tipped; and distinguished from all other Virginia mice by the extremely long tail and long hind legs.

Distribution in Virginia.—State-wide, but perhaps most numerous west of the Blue Ridge.

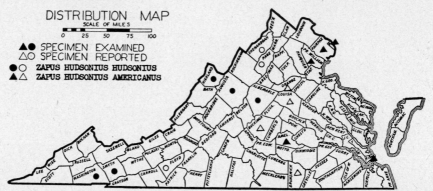

Fig. 96—Distribution of the meadow jumping mice, *Zapus hudsonius hudsonius* and *Zapus hudsonius americanus*, in Virginia.

Subspecies in Virginia

Zapus hudsonius hudsonius (Zimmerman)

Type Locality.—Hudson Bay, Canada.

Distinguishing Characteristics.—Distinguished from *Zapus h. americanus* by brighter coloration and better defined dorsal stripe.

Measurements.—Two adults from Highland County, Virginia, average: Total length, 215 mm.; tail vertebrae, 132 mm.; hind foot, 29.5 mm.

General Distribution.—Southeastern Canada and northeastern United States; limits of range not known.

Distribution in Virginia.—The western mountainous portion of the State; common in some sections, rare in others. See figure 96.

Habitat.—Thick vegetation such as sedges, asters, or other annual herbs, usually near or beside running water; occurring both in woodland and farmland wherever the habitat is suitable.

Remarks.—Virginia specimens are not clearly referable to *hudsonius,* but until the genus is revised there is no other name available. We have not seen specimens from the northern mountain region (Shenandoah and Page Counties) which A. H. Howell called *americanus;* specimens at hand from further south (Highland and Albemarle Counties) are definitely not referable to *americanus.*

Zapus hudsonius americanus   (Barton)

Type Locality.—Near Philadelphia, Pennsylvania.

Distinguishing Characteristics.—Similar to *hudsonius,* but smaller, and dorsal band less distinct, lacking most of the black seen in *hudsonius;* upper parts deep dull orange rather than yellowish as in *hudsonius.*

Measurements.—One adult from Amelia, Virginia: Total length, 198 mm.; tail vertebrae, 122 mm.; hind foot, 28 mm.

General Distribution.—Coastal Plain and Piedmont of the Atlantic seaboard from southern Connecticut south to northern South Carolina.

Distribution in Virginia.—Coastal plain and Piedmont; also reported from the northern mountain section. Uncommon. See figure 96.

Habitat.—This subspecies has been so rarely caught in Virginia that no habitat preference has been noted. It seems worthwhile, therefore, to note the following specific points of capture: near Falls Church, in Fairfax County, J. H. Riley observed several in a dry field of thick broom sedge, and C. K. Rorebeck caught one in a similar situation; at Amelia Court House, J. A. King caught one near a drainage ditch covered with honeysuckle and blackberry in a small thicket between a highway and a railroad; in southeastern Brunswick County, J. B. Lewis caught one in a heavy growth of cattail and swamp grasses and sedges in swampy lowgrounds.

Remarks.—The jumping mice are the only Virginia mice that hibernate during the winter months.

Napaeozapus insignis roanensis   (Preble)

Woodland Jumping Mouse

Type Locality.—Roan Mountain, Mitchell County, North Carolina.

Distinguishing Characteristics.—Outwardly similar to *Zapus,* but larger and brighter orange and with tail white tipped. Upper parts a mixture of bright orange and black, the orange most concentrated on the sides, and the black in a wide, sharply defined band on the back; underparts pure white; tail grayish above, white below, white tipped; feet brownish white.

Measurements.—Average of five adults from Mountain Lake, Giles County, Virginia: Total length, 222.8 mm. (219-227 mm.); tail vertebrae, 135.8 mm. (132-139 mm.); hind foot, 30.0 mm. (30-30 mm.).

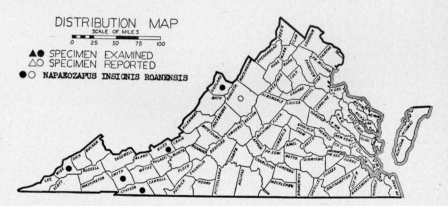

Fig. 97.—Distribution of the woodland jumping mouse, *Napaeazapus insignis roanensis,* in Virginia.

General Distribution.—The Appalachian Highlands from North Carolina and Tennessee north to western Maryland.

Distribution in Virginia.—The Allegheny Mountains; has not been taken in the Blue Ridge, probably because of lack of collecting in that region. Locally common to abundant; C. O. Handley, Jr. and his father took 21 *Napaeozapus* and 10 *Zapus* in three nights trapping in Highland County in September, 1943. See figure 97.

Habitat.—Moist, cool, rocky woodlands. We have found it most abundant at high altitudes among ferns, blackberry, and St. John's-wort in clearings surrounded by forest.

Family **Erethizontidae**

Erethizon dorsatum dorsatum   (Linnaeus)

Porcupine

Type Locality.—Eastern Canada.

Distinguishing Characteristics.—Size large (1000 mm.); tail short and thick; pelage intermixed with long sharp quills or spines; general coloration, slaty black. Distinguished from all other Virginia mammals by the long sharp quills.

Measurements.—"Total length, 36-40 inches (1000 mm.); tail vertebrae, 6 inches (150 mm.); hind foot, 3.5-4 inches (100 mm.)" (Anthony 1928).

General Distribution.—Northern North America from Nova Scotia south to Pennsylvania and westward and northwestward to the Great Lakes region and the Arctic Circle.

Distribution in Virginia.—In 1739, John Clayton of Gloucester County wrote ". . . . there has been two Porcupines killed here, but they are very scarce" [*Virginia Historical Magazine,* 7(2): 172-174; 1899]. We are not sure whether this refers to a locality in Virginia or one in what is now West Virginia, but at such an early date, when West Virginia territory was only just beginning to be reached by settlers, it seems reasonable to believe that the specimens referred to came from Virginia. There have been recent reports of the porcupine on Spruce Knob, Pendleton County, West Virginia, but residents of nearby Highland County, Virginia, do not know of its occurrence in that part of Virginia. There can be little doubt, however, that it did once occur in Virginia, since its remains have been found as far south as Tennessee.

Habitat.—Forests of spruce, hemlock and birch.

Order **LAGOMORPHA**

Key to the Order

1. Coloration white. *Lepus americanus* (winter), page 186.
   Coloration brown. (2)

2. Underside of the tail dark. *Sylvilagus palustris,* page 190.
   Underside of the tail white. (3)

3. Length of hind foot more than 100 mm.; as much as 150 mm. *Lepus americanus,* page 186.
   Length of hind foot less than 100 mm. (4)

4. Black on the forward edge of the ear sharply defined from the brown of the rest of the ear. *Sylvilagus transitionalis,* page 189.
   Black on the forward edge of the ear not sharply defined from the brown of the rest of the ear. *Sylvilagus floridanus,* page 187.

Family **Leporidae**

Lepus americanus virginianus Harlan

Varying Hare

Type Locality.—The Blue Mountains, northeast to Harrisburg, Pennsylvania.

Distinguishing Characteristics.—Size medium (525 mm.); hind feet large; fur dense; pelage reddish brown in summer, white in winter. Distinguished from *Sylvilagus* by much larger size. Its presence in a region can be most easily discovered in the winter time when the ground is covered with snow, for its tracks are almost exactly twice as large as those of the common cottontail; tracks of the large hind foot of the hare measure 5 inches in length in the snow, while those of the cottontail measure but 2½ inches.

Measurements.—"Total length, 20-21 inches (525 mm.); tail vertebrae, 2 inches (50 mm.); hind foot, 5.5 inches (140 mm.)." (Anthony 1928.)

General Distribution.—Extreme southern Ontario, Canada and northeastern United States from north central Maine south to the Allegheny Mountains of Virginia and West Virginia, and possibly as far south as the Great Smoky Mountains of North Carolina and Tennessee.

Distribution in Virginia.—Probably formerly occurred throughout the mountainous portion of the State at higher elevations; now known to occur only in Highland County, where it is uncommon. See figure 99.

Habitat.—More or less restricted to areas of spruce and fir, where it is found in open woods and thickets.

Remarks.—The varying hare is a fine game animal, and efforts should be made to re-establish it in suitable places in Virginia, such as Whitetop, Mount Rogers, and Mountain Lake.

186

Sylvilagus floridanus

Cottontail

General Description.—Size small (425 mm.); ears long; upper parts reddish brown, darkest on back; underparts white; underside of tail white. Distinguished from *Sylvilagus transitionalis* by larger size, longer ears and more reddish coloration; from *Sylvilagus palustris* by the white "cottontail"; and from *Lepus a. virginianus* by much smaller size.

Distribution in Virginia.—State-wide.

Fig. 98.—Distribution of the cottontail, *Sylvilagus floridanus hitchensi, Sylvilagus floridanus mallurus,* and *Sylvilagus floridanus mearnsi,* in Virginia.

Subspecies in Virginia

Sylvilagus floridanus hitchensi Mearns

Type Locality.—Smith's Island, Northampton County, Virginia.

Distinguishing Characteristics.—An insular form similar to *Sylvilagus f. mallurus,* but distinguished from it by paler, less contrasting, sandy brown coloration, almost complete lack of a black stripe on the anterior margin of the ears, and by heavier, coarser hair which gives it a shaggy appearance.

Measurements.—Three Virginia specimens average: Total length, 425 mm. (375-477 mm.); tail vertebrae, 58.3 mm. (50-70 mm.); hind foot, 94.0 mm. (90-97 mm.); ear from notch (dried), 55.5 mm. (54-57 mm.). (Llewellyn and Handley 1945).

General Distribution.—Known only from Smith's Island and Fisherman's Island, off the Atlantic coast of Northampton County, Virginia. See figure 98.

Habitat.—Brush and marsh borders.

Remarks.—L. M. Llewellyn and C. O. Handley speculate that the Hitchens' cottontail may have been exterminated by the great storm of 1933 which temporarily inundated many of the coastal islands. Information at hand seems to indicate that at least on Fisherman's Island it no longer exists.

Sylvilagus floridanus mallurus (Thomas)

Type Locality.—Raleigh, Wake County, North Carolina.

Distinguishing Characteristics.—Similar to *Sylvilagus f. mearnsi,* but slightly darker and more reddish.

Measurements.—Average of 152 adults from Virginia: Total length, 426.9 mm. (320-500 mm.); tail vertebrae, 48.9 mm. (25-65 mm.); hind foot, 94.1 mm. (83-110 mm.); ear from notch, 62.5 mm. (56-70 mm.). (Llewellyn and Handley 1945).

General Distribution.—Atlantic and Gulf Coast States from Connecticut south to central interior Florida and west to eastern Tennessee and Alabama.

Distribution in Virginia.—The whole State east of the Tennessee River watershed; that is, east of Tazewell and Smyth Counties. Abundant. See figure 98.

Habitat.—Farmlands, brushlands, woods, and gardens, usually in dry situations.

Sylvilagus floridanus mearnsi (Allen)

Type Locality.—Fort Snelling, Hennepin County, Minnesota.

Distinguishing Characteristics.—Almost indistinguishable from *Sylvilagus f. mallurus,* but typical specimens show a somewhat paler, grayer, less rufous, coloration of the back, a slightly grayer rump, and a somewhat duller nape.

Measurements.—Average of 23 adults from southwest Virginia: Total length, 422.9 mm. (330-483 mm.); tail vertebrae, 49.1 mm. (42-60 mm.); hind foot, 95.1 mm. (90-102 mm.); ear from notch, 62.6 mm. (55-71 mm.). (Llewellyn and Handley 1945).

General Distribution.—Central United States and southern Canada from western Virginia, western New York, and southern Ontario west to southern Minnesota and south to northeastern Kansas and north central Tennessee.

Distribution in Virginia.—Typical *Sylvilagus f. mearnsi* does not occur in Virginia but Llewellyn and Handley (1945) have referred specimens from the southwestern counties of Lee, Wise, Dickenson, Scott, Russell and western Tazewell to this race. For the sake of convenience, we have considered the western edge of the New River drainage system to be the eastern limit for this subspecies. See figure 98.

Habitat.—Farmlands, brushlands, woods and gardens, usually in dry situations.

Sylvilagus transitionalis (Bangs)

New England Cottontail

Type Locality.—Liberty Hill, New London County, Connecticut.

Distinguishing Characteristics.—Similar to *Sylvilagus floridanus,* but distinguished from it by considerably smaller size, and noticeably shorter ears with sharply defined black anterior margins (*Sylvilagus floridanus* also has the anterior margin black, but it grades gradually into the brown of the remainder of the ear and is not sharply defined). Distinguished from the varying hare by much smaller size.

Measurements.—Three adults from Highland County average: Total length, 403 mm. (390-410 mm.); tail vertebrae, 50.7 mm. (50-51 mm.); hind foot, 91.7 mm. (90-94 mm.); ear from notch, 58.7 mm. (58-60 mm.).

General Distribution. —From southern Maine and northern Vermont south in the Appalachian Highlands to northeastern Alabama.

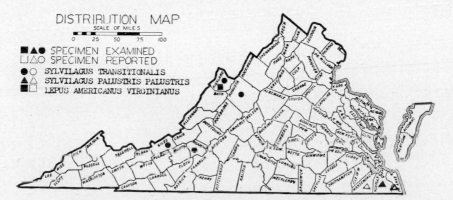

Fig. 99.—Distribution of the New England cottontail, *Sylvilagus transitionalis;* the marsh rabbit, *Sylvilagus palustris palustris;* and the varying hare, *Lepus americanus virginianus,* in Virginia.

Distribution in Virginia.—At higher altitudes throughout the mountainous portion of the State; probably does not occur below 2500 feet elevation. See figure 99.

Habitat.—Woods or brushy country on the upper slopes of mountains; thought to be more of a woods rabbit than *Sylvilagus floridanus.*

Remarks.—In the western part of the State it is not unusual to find the New England and Eastern cottontail inhabiting the same territory.

Sylvilagus palustris palustris (Bachman)
Marsh Rabbit

Type Locality.—Eastern South Carolina.

Distinguishing Characteristics.—About the same size as *Sylvilagus floridanus,* but much darker and lacking the white "cottontail." The toenails of the hind feet are conspicuous and the feet appear small because of the absence of the heavy covering of hair found in other races of *Sylvilagus* from Virginia.

Measurements.—Two adults from the Dismal Swamp, Virginia, average: "Total length, 447.5 mm.; tail vertebrae, 40.0 mm.; hind foot, 99.0 mm." (Llewellyn and Handley 1945).

General Distribution.—Lowlands along the rivers and coasts of the southeastern states from southeastern Virginia south to northern Florida and west along the Gulf Coast to Mobile Bay, Alabama.

Distribution in Virginia.—Known only from the three southeastern counties of Nansemond, Norfolk and Princess Anne. Common. See figure 99.

Habitat.—Swamps and fresh-water marshes, often found in and about cane brakes.

Remarks.—The marsh rabbit and the cottontail are seldom found together since the marsh rabbit prefers the same moist ground which is shunned by the cottontail.

W. H. Burt photo   *Courtesy Univ. Mich. Mus. Zool.*

Fig. 100.—White-tailed Deer buck.

Order **ARTIODACTYLA**

Key to the Order

Tail light colored on both upper and lower surfaces; main beam of antlers directed rearward, tines point forward. *Cervus canadensis,* page 191.

Tail white beneath, darker on upper surfaces; main beams of antlers directed forward, tines point rearward. *Odocoileus virginianus,* page 192.

Family **Cervidae**

Cervus canadensis

Elk

General Description.—A large deer, characterized by widely branching antlers, chestnut brown coloration, except for a straw colored rump patch, and a short mane on the neck. Bulls considerably larger than cows, and the cow lacking antlers.

Distribution in Virginia.—Formerly state-wide; now restricted to limited areas in the mountains where it has been restocked.

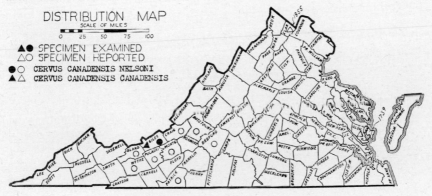

Fig. 101.—Distribution of the elk, *Cervus canadensis canadensis* and *Cervus canadensis nelsoni,* in Virginia. Figures indicate last dates of reports of *Cervus c. canadensis.*

Subspecies in Virginia

Cervus canadensis canadensis Erxleben

Type Locality.—Eastern Canada.

Distinguishing Characteristics.—Somewhat smaller than the western subspecies *nelsoni* and brighter and darker in coloration.

191

Measurements.—Total length, about 8 ft.; tail vertebrae, 5½ in.; hind foot, 25 in.; height at shoulder, 4½ ft.; weight, 500-600 lbs.

General Distribution.—Formerly ranged over eastern North America from southern Quebec and western New England south to northern Alabama, and west to Arkansas and Minnesota. Now probably extinct.

Distribution in Virginia.—Though formerly abundant throughout the State, the last native elk was apparently killed in 1855 in Clarke County. See figure 101. Skulls are occasionally found in limestone caves.

Habitat.—Wooded regions.

Cervus canadensis nelsoni Bailey

Type Locality.—Yellowstone National Park, Wyoming.

Distinguishing Characteristics.—Similar to *Cervus c. canadensis,* but larger in both size of body and antlers, and somewhat paler in color.

Measurements.—Adult males may weigh as much as 600 lbs. and measure 8 or 9 feet in total length.

General Distribution.—The Rocky Mountains from northern New Mexico north to central Alberta, and formerly possibly the Great Plains area also. In recent years it has been successfully introduced in many areas outside its former range.

Distribution in Virginia—Two small herds of elk restocked from Yellowstone National Park in 1917 and in 1935 are established in Bland and Giles Counties and in Botetourt and Bedford Counties. Wanderers from these herds have been recorded in Craig, Montgomery, Pulaski, Patrick and Wythe Counties and may be expected anywhere in southwest Virginia. See figure 101.

Habitat.—In the Rocky Mountains it summers in the forests and meadows of the high slopes and winters in the open valleys. Here in Virginia it has survived only in the wildest mountains, where it finds safe havens in the thick brush, and only occasionally does it venture out into mountain fields during the day.

Odocoileus virginianus virginianus (Boddaert)

White-tailed Deer

Type Locality.—Eastern Virginia.

Distinguishing Characteristics.—Size large (1825 mm.), but considerably smaller than the elk; antlers large, and the main beam directed forward; upper parts of body reddish brown in summer, grayish in winter; underparts and underside of tail white.

Measurements.—Large males average about as follows: Total length, 6 ft. (1825 mm.); tail vertebrae, 10 in. (250 mm.); hind foot, 20 in. (500 mm.); weight, 150-200 lbs. Does are considerably smaller.

General Distribution.—The southeastern United States from central Pennsylvania and New Jersey south to east central Florida, and west to southern Indiana and northern Alabama. Another subspecies inhabits the Gulf Coast region.

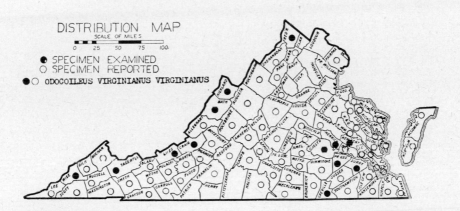

Fig. 102.—Distribution of the white-tailed deer, *Odocoileus virginianus virginianus*, in Virginia.

Distribution in Virginia.—The deer once had state-wide distribution, but by 1905 it had been exterminated in 44 of the mountain and Piedmont counties. However, between 1926 and 1943, a total of 1,285 deer, largely from Pennsylvania, Wisconsin, North Carolina, and Michigan, were released at suitable points in the mountain counties. This restocking program met with almost complete success and deer are once again found in 80 of Virginia's 100 counties. Despite this restocking, however, deer are still most numerous in the great river swamps of the Tidewater section and in Bath and Highland Counties, where native stocks have survived. See figure 102.

Habitat.—Forests.

Remarks.—Among the 1,285 deer released in the restocking program up until March 1943 were 516 deer which were considered to be the larger northern subspecies, *Odocoileus v. borealis.* In just one county (Buchanan), however, was only *borealis* released. In all other counties where *borealis* was released, nearly equal or greater numbers of *virginianus* were also released. Thus, it does not seem likely or even possible that the *borealis* stock could long remain isolated and recognizable. For that reason *borealis* has not been given a place on the list as one of the mammals of Virginia.

Family Bovidae

Bison bison bison   (Linnaeus)

Bison

Type Locality.—Northeast Mexico.

Distinguishing Characteristics.—Body large and heavy, humped at the shoulder, horns short and incurved, foreparts covered with long shaggy brown hair, rest of body with shorter lighter colored hair. Bulls considerably larger than cows.

Measurements.—Total length, 7-11 ft. (2134-3353 mm.); tail vertebrae, 18-24 in. (457-610 mm.); hind foot, 20-24 in. (508-610 mm.); height at shoulder, 5-6 ft. (1521-1825 mm.); weight, bulls, 1800-2000 lbs., cows, 800-1000 lbs.

General Distribution.—Formerly from northeast Mexico north to Alberta and Saskatchewan, and east to central New York and central Georgia. No longer occurs in the wild state.

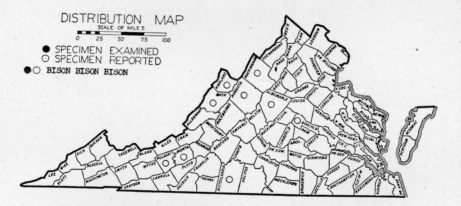

Fig. 103.—Former distribution of the bison, *Bison bison bison,* in Virginia.

Distribution in Virginia.—Once fairly common in the western half of the State; the last one was killed along New River in 1797 (Coues 1871). See figure 103.

Habitat.—Plains and open land. In Virginia it was often found in thick woods but preferred the openings in the valleys.

Order SIRENIA

Family Trichechidae

Trichechus manatus latirostris (Harlan)

Manatee

Type Locality.—Near the Capes of East Florida.

Distinguishing Characteristics.—Size large, a little larger than a dolphin; body very heavy, robust, and rounded; upper lips thick and large and muzzle blunt; forelegs modified into broad flippers, hind legs not visible; tail broad and rounded, horizontally flattened; practically hairless except for a few bristles on the muzzle; coloration of skin gray black. Distinguished from all other aquatic mammals by the flat, broad, rounded tail.

Measurements.—Adults measure 7-15 feet in total length, about 3 feet in width of tail, and weigh from 500-1,500 pounds. Calves are 2-3 feet long at birth.

General Distribution.—East coast of Florida north to St. Augustine and up the west coast a little north of Cape Sable; has occasionally wandered along the coast in summer as far west as Louisiana and as far north as North Carolina and Virginia.

Distribution in Virginia.—Recorded on the basis of Nelson's (1916) statement that it has strayed "as far north as the coast of Virginia." This seems creditable since H. H. Brimley in 1931 reported one which had been caught at Wilmington, North Carolina, only about 200 miles south of our borders.

Habitat.—Tropical coastal waters, lagoons, bays and rivers; straying to cooler waters during summer.

Order **CETACEA**

Key to the Order

1. Dorsal fin missing. (2)
   Dorsal fin present. (3)

2. Lower jaws toothed. *Physeter catodon*, page 200.
   Lower jaws not toothed. *Balaena glacialis*, page 197.

3. Dorsal fin posterior to the middle of the back. (4)
   Dorsal fin in the middle of the back or forward of the middle. (10)

4. Lower jaws with at least two teeth. (5)
   Lower jaws not toothed. (7)

5. Snout large and protruding in front of lower jaws. *Kogia breviceps*, page 200.
   Snout narrow and flattened, forming a "beak"; lower jaw protruding in front of snout. (6)

6. Total length of adult more than twenty feet. *Ziphius cavirostris*, page 206.
   Total length of adult less than twenty feet. *Mesoplodon mirus*, page 205.

7. Pectoral fins long, equalling or exceeding the distance from the eye to the end of the snout. *Megaptera novaeangliae*, page 199.
   Pectoral fins short, equaling hardly more than half the distance from the eye to the end of the snout. (8)

8. Rostrum, viewed from above, somewhat U-shaped. *Sibbaldus musculus*, page 199.
   Rostrum, viewed from above, somewhat V-shaped. (9)

9. Baleen plates entirely black, with inner bristles white; total length not more than 56 feet. *Balaenoptera borealis*, page 198.
   Baleen plates particolored, streaked with purple and white; total length may be as much as 80 feet. *Balaenoptera physalus*, page 197.

10. Snout flattened to form a beak. (11)
    Snout not flattened; beak lacking. (16)

11. Forehead swollen and protruding in front of beak. (12)
    Forehead not swollen; forehead sloping back smoothly from beak. (13)

12. Pectoral fin relatively long, equaling about one-fifth of total length of body. *Globicephala ventricosa*, page 204.
    Pectoral fin relatively short, equaling about one-sixth or less of total length of body. *Globicephala brachyptera*, page 204.

13. Beak not marked off from forehead by transverse groove. *Steno rostratus*, page 201.
    Beak marked off from forehead by transverse groove. (14)

14. Eyes conspicuously ringed with white. *Delphinus delphis*, page 202.
    Eyes not conspicuously ringed with white. (15)

15. Upper parts heavily sprinkled with small white spots. *Stenella plagiodon*, page 201.
    Upper parts not spotted. *Tursiops truncatus*, page 202.

16. Coloration uniformly black throughout. *Pseudorca crassidens*, page 203.
    Coloration black only on back. (17)

17. Size large; 15-30 feet in total length. *Grampus orca*, page 203.
    Size small; 4-6 feet in total length. *Phocaena phocaena*, page 205.

Suborder MYSTACOCETI

Family Balaenidae

Balaena glacialis (Borowski)

Right Whale

Type Locality.—North Sea.

Distinguishing Characteristics.—Size medium for whale (50 feet); blades of baleen, or whalebone, in the mouth, narrow and black; lower lips large and fleshy; end of muzzle crowned by a horny, irregular bump; dorsal fin and furrows on the skin of the throat absent; coloration often entirely black, though some individuals are white bellied. The spout, caused by the moisture laden exhalation of breath through the nostrils or blowholes, is directed forward and upward as high as fifteen feet in twin columns forming a V. Distinguished from other large whales likely to occur in Virginia waters by the absence of the dorsal fin, and by the V-shaped spout.

Measurements.—Adults measure 45-55 feet in length at maturity. The longest of the whalebones measure 6-7 feet.

General Distribution. The North Atlantic Ocean, south in European waters to the Bay of Biscay and in American waters to South Carolina.

Distribution in Virginia.—Reynard (1889) writes: "In the fall of 1856, Dr. P. A. Taliaferro, with a double-barreled shotgun, killed a Greenland or right whale in North River, Va., an estuary of Mobjack Bay which opens into the Chesapeake between New Point Comfort and the mouth of York River on York Spit (Gloucester County). The whale was forty-six feet long, and if I remember correctly, girthed twenty feet." This whale, like the other North Atlantic Cetaceans, may be expected along the Virginia coasts at any time.

Habitat.—Temperate and sub-frigid seas.

Family Balaenopteridae

Balaenoptera physalus (Linnaeus)

Finback Whale

Type Locality.—Spitzbergen seas.

Distinguishing Characteristics.—Size large for a whale (70 feet); throat furrowed; whalebones not long; dorsal fin small; coloration of upper parts dark gray, of underparts snowy white; baleen plates particolored, streaked with purple and white. Spout a vertical, elongated ellipse, 15 to 20 feet in height, issued with an accompanying peculiar and characteristic whistling metallic sound. Distinguished from *Balaenoptera borealis* by larger size and streaking of baleen, and from other large whales by the small pectoral fin and presence of whalebones and dorsal fin.

Measurements.—Adults measure 60-80 feet in total length at maturity, and calves about 21 feet at birth. Average weight of adults is about 70 tons. The longest whalebones measure 2-3 feet in length.

General Distribution.—All large seas. This is one of the commonest whales along the east coast of the United States.

Distribution in Virginia.—A specimen was caught in Mobjack Bay, Gloucester County, in May 1866 (Allen 1869). Another large whale which was stranded on a sandbar in Cobbs Channel, Northampton County, in the 1880's may have been of this species (Barret, *Richmond News Leader,* March 25, 1935).

Habitat.—Temperate and sub-frigid seas.

Balaenoptera borealis Lesson
Sei Whale

Type Locality.—Gromitz, Lubeck Bay, Schleswig-Holstein, Germany.

Distinguishing Characteristics.—Size medium for a whale (50 feet); throat furrowed; dorsal fin fairly large, larger and higher than that of *Balaenoptera physalus*; coloration of upper parts and flanks gray, dark steel gray, or bluish gray; underparts white; body often bears many small oblong white scars left by copepod parasites; baleen plates entirely black, with inner bristles white. Spout a vertical cone-shaped column as much as 10 feet in height. Distinguished from *Balaenoptera physalus* by smaller size and black baleen, and from other large whales by the small pectoral fins and by the presence of the dorsal fin and whalebones.

Measurements.—Adults range from 40-55 feet in total length. Calves are about 15 feet long at birth.

General Distribution.—Atlantic and Pacific Oceans between the Arctic and Antarctic Circles.

Distribution in Virginia.—An immature male, 26 feet 4 inches long, washed ashore at Walnut Point, Northumberland County, in March 1923 (Miller 1927). This was the second North American record for the species.

Habitat.—Temperate and tropical seas.

Sibbaldus musculus (Linnaeus)
Blue Whale

Type Locality.—Firth of Forth, Scotland.

Distinguishing Characteristics.—Size large (75 feet), the largest of the whales; dorsal fin small and placed far back on the body; upper parts dark gray or blackish; underparts lighter, sometimes spotted with white; baleen black, two to three feet long. Distinguished from *Balaenoptera physalus*, the only other baleen whale of similar size that might occur with frequency in Virginia waters, by having the rostrum somewhat U-shaped when viewed from above.

Measurements.—Sixty to eighty feet in total length; 60 tons in weight. Large individuals 100 feet and 150 tons.

General Distribution.—Arctic and North Atlantic and Pacific Oceans.

Distribution in Virginia.—Not recorded.

Habitat.—Cold and temperate seas.

Megaptera novaeangliae (Borowski)
Humpback Whale

Type Locality.—Coast of New England.

Distinguishing Characteristics.—Size medium for a whale (45 feet); body short and thickset; pectoral fins or foreflippers long, equalling the distance from the eye to the end of the snout; snout, lower jaws, and pectoral fins with rows of small, fleshy, rounded knobs; head flattened; throat furrowed; whalebone short; coloration black, except for throat and breast which are white. Spout is vertical, plume-like, and as much as 20 feet high. Distinguished from other large whales by the short, thick body, and long pectoral fins.

Measurements.—Adults measure 40-50 feet in total length and average about 45 tons in weight; calves 15 feet at birth.

General Distribution.—All large seas.

Distribution in Virginia.—Recorded on the basis of Stone's (1907) statement that "it has been taken as far south as Virginia." No specimens have been located.

Habitat.—Both warm and frigid seas.

Suborder ODONTOCETI

Family Physeteridae

Physeter catodon Linnaeus
Sperm Whale

Type Locality.—Kairston, Orkney Islands.

Distinguishing Characteristics.—Size medium for a whale (50 feet); lower jaws narrow and slender, and dwarfed by the enormous, square-angled snout which protrudes ahead of the lower jaws; eyes relatively large; lower jaws toothed; whalebone and dorsal fin absent. Spout plume-like and directed diagonally forward. Distinguished from all other large whales by the huge snout.

Measurements.—Adults measure 40-55 feet in length; average 45 tons in weight. Calves are about 13 feet long at birth.

General Distribution.—All large seas between the Arctic and Antarctic Circles.

Distribution in Virginia.—Not recorded, but to be expected.

Habitat.—Warm seas.

Kogia breviceps (Blainville)
Pigmy Sperm Whale

Type Locality.—Region of the Cape of Good Hope, South Africa.

Distinguishing Characteristics.—Size small for a whale (8 feet); snout bluntly pointed and protruding in front of lower jaws; lower jaws with numerous teeth; dorsal fin near middle of total length; coloration of upper parts black, underparts light gray or grayish white. The combination of small size, protruding snout, and toothed lower jaws distinguish this species.

Measurements.—Adults average about 8 feet in length and weigh 1000 pounds, but large individuals may measure as much as 13 feet.

General Distribution.—All warm seas; north on the Atlantic coast of North America to Nova Scotia.

Distribution in Virginia.—It has been found in the vicinity of Cape Henry, Princess Anne County, four times in early spring.

Habitat.—Warm seas.

Family Delphinidae

Stenella plagiodon (Cope)
Spotted Dolphin

Type Locality.—Unknown.

Distinguishing Characteristics.—Size about average for a dolphin (6 feet); both upper and lower jaws toothed; beak rather long, and marked off from forehead by a transverse groove; coloration of upper parts purplish gray or grayish black, marked with many small white spots; underparts pale gray. The numerous white spots on the back and flanks distinguish *Stenella plagiodon* from other beaked dolphins.

Measurements.—Adults vary from 5 to 7 feet in total length.

General Distribution.—Along east coast of the United States from North Carolina to Texas.

Distribution in Virginia.—Not recorded, but should be expected.

Habitat.—Warm seas.

Steno rostratus Gray
Rough-toothed Dolphin

Type Locality.—North Sea.

Distinguishing Characteristics.—Size average for a dolphin (7 feet); beak slender, flattened from side to side rather than from above; beak not marked off from the forehead by a transverse groove; both upper and lower jaws toothed; crowns of teeth with fine vertical wrinkles; coloration of upper parts slaty black; underparts, including all of beak, white; back may be spotted with white scars. Distinguished from other beaked dolphins by absence of the groove at the base of the beak and by the rough teeth.

Measurements.—Adults reach a maximum of 7-8 feet in total length.

General Distribution.—Atlantic, Pacific, and Indian Oceans, in temperate waters.

Distribution in Virginia.—U. S. National Museum specimen no. 7458 was taken at Norfolk, Norfolk County, sometime prior to 1867. This is one of the very few North American records for the species.

Habitat.—Warm seas.

Delphinus delphis Linnaeus

Common Dolphin

Type Locality.—European seas.

Distinguishing Characteristics.—Size average for a dolphin (7 feet); both upper and lower jaws toothed; coloration of upper parts and pectoral fins black, flanks yellowish, underparts white; eyes ringed with white and the white extending in two lines around the front of the head along the groove which marks off the beak from the forehead. The white ringed eyes and yellow flanks distinguish this from other similar dolphins.

Measurements.—Adults measure 7-8 feet in total length.

General Distribution.—Warm and temperate parts of the north Atlantic Ocean and adjacent smaller seas.

Distribution in Virginia.—Specimens were taken at Cobb's Island, Northampton County, and at Dam Neck Mills, Princess Anne County, prior to 1887. It should occur rather frequently on the Virginia coast.

Habitat.—Warm and temperate seas.

Tursiops truncatus (Montague)

Bottle-nosed Dolphin

Type Locality.—Totness, Devonshire, England.

Distinguishing Characteristics.—Size rather large for a dolphin (10 feet); beak marked off from forehead by a transverse groove; beak relatively short; both upper and lower jaws toothed; coloration of upper parts purplish lead gray; underparts lighter gray. Large size and uniform grayish coloration separate *Tursiops truncatus* from other similar dolphins.

Measurements.—Adults measure 9-12 feet in total length.

General Distribution.—Atlantic Ocean and adjacent smaller seas; the most common dolphin along the east coast of the United States.

Distribution in Virginia.—It has been recorded several times from Cherrystone Point (Matthews County?); Smith's Island, Northampton County; Ocean View, Norfolk County; Virginia Beach, Princess Anne County; Buff Point, Westmoreland County, and in the vicinity of Washington, D. C. It is the most commonly occurring marine mammal in Virginia waters.

Habitat.—Warm seas.

Grampus orca (Linnaeus)
Killer Whale

Type Locality.—European seas.

Distinguishing Characteristics.—Size of small whale (20 feet); body heavy and powerful; tail and pectoral fins large; dorsal fin large and erect; both upper and lower jaws armed with large teeth; not beaked; coloration of head and back jet black; underparts and a patch behind the eye snowy white. Distinguished from other whales and porpoises by the large erect dorsal fin, large murderous teeth, and sharply contrasting black and white coloration.

Measurements.—Adults measure 15-30 feet in total length.

General Distribution.—Cosmopolitan.

Distribution in Virginia.—Not recorded, but to be expected.

Habitat.—Frigid, temperate and tropical seas.

Pseudorca crassidens (Owen)
False Killer Whale

Type Locality.—Lincolnshire Fens, England.

Distinguishing Characteristics.—Size of small whale (15 feet); dorsal fin relatively small and recurved, and located just forward of the middle of the back; pectoral fins narrow and tapering; head flattened; snout bluntly rounded; beak lacking; both upper and lower jaws toothed; coloration uniformly black, sometimes spotted with light colored scars. Distinguished from *Globicephala*, the only other solid black whale, by the rearward position of the dorsal fin and by the lack of the bulging forehead.

Measurements.—Adults average 15-18 feet in total length.

General Distribution.—All seas except near the poles.

Distribution in Virginia—Not recorded but should be expected.

Habitat.—Cold, temperate and tropical seas.

Globicephala ventricosa (Lacepede)
Blackfish

Type Locality.—Scapay Bay, Pomona, Orkney Islands, Scotland.

Distinguishing Characteristics.—Size of small whale (20 feet); dorsal fin large and recurved and set far forward on back; pectoral fins long, equal to about one-fifth of total length of body; beak very short; forehead almost globular and protruding in front of the beak; both upper and lower jaws toothed; coloration uniformly black, or black with only a narrow stripe of white extending from the throat to the belly. Spout about five feet high. Distinguished from *Globicephala brachyptera* by longer pectoral fin, and from *Pseudorca crassidens* by the bulging forehead and forward position of the dorsal fin.

Measurements.—Adults measure 14-28 feet in total length; calves, 5-6 feet at birth.

General Distribution.—Temperate and tropical portions of the Atlantic and Pacific Oceans.

Distribution in Virginia.—It has been taken at Cape Henry, Princess Anne County; Smith's Island, Northampton County; and Chincoteague Island, Accomac County.

Habitat.—Temperate and tropical seas.

Globicephala brachyptera (Cope)
Short-finned Blackfish

Type Locality.—Delaware Bay.

Distinguishing Characteristics.—Similar in form, size, and coloration to *Globicephala ventricosa,* but pectoral fin short, equalling only about one-sixth or less of the total length of the body.

Measurements.—Adults measure 15-20 feet in total length. An adult male reported by True (1889) as taken at Dam Neck Mills, Princess Anne County, Virginia, measured 15 feet, 3 inches in total length, and had the pectoral fin 30 inches long from base to tip (16.9% of total length of body).

General Distribution.—The West Indies and the Atlantic coast of North America from New Jersey to the Gulf of Mexico.

Distribution in Virginia.—A specimen was taken at Dam Neck Mills, Princess Anne County, in 1887.

Habitat.—Warm seas.

Phocaena phocaena (Linnaeus)
Harbor Porpoise

Type Locality.—Swedish seas.

Distinguishing Characteristics.—Size small (5 feet); body short and heavy-set; dorsal fin relatively small; snout blunt and rounded; beak lacking; both upper and lower jaws toothed; coloration of upper parts, including lips of lower jaws, black; underparts white. Distinguished from other dolphins of similar size by lack of a beak and by the chubby body.

Measurements.—Adults measure 4-6 feet in total length. Calves are 2-3 feet long at birth.

General Distribution.—North Atlantic Ocean south to Gibraltar and New Jersey.

Distribution in Virginia. Not recorded, but might be expected.

Habitat.—Cold and temperate waters close to shore; sometimes ascends rivers.

Family **Ziphiidae**

Mesoplodon mirus True
True's Beaked Whale

Type Locality.—Beaufort Harbor, Carteret County, North Carolina.

Distinguishing Characteristics. Size small for a whale (17 feet); throat marked by two anteriorly converging grooves which form a ∧; dorsal fin set far back on the back; each lower jaw with a single tooth at the anterior end; in the female, teeth short and concealed in the gums; coloration of upper parts slaty black, underparts lighter. Smaller size and darker coloration distinguish *Mesoplodon mirus* from the somewhat similar *Ziphius cavirostris*.

Measurements.—Adults average about 17 feet in length and weigh 2,000-3,000 pounds. Calves are 7-8 feet long at birth.

General Distribution.—Southeast coast of the United States.

Distribution in Virginia.—Not recorded, but to be expected.

Habitat.—Temperate seas.

Ziphius cavirostris G. Cuvier
Cuvier's Beaked Whale

Type Locality.—Near Fos, Bôuches-du-Rhone, France.

Distinguishing Characteristics.—Size small for a whale (22 feet); body thickset; throat marked with anteriorly converging grooves forming a ∧; caudal flukes not separated by a distinct notch; lower jaws each with a single tooth at the forward end; back marked with a conspicuous medial keel from dorsal fin to tail; coloration variable, some specimens having head, neck, and forward portion of back white and the remainder of the body gray, others are purplish black above, spotted or brown on the sides, and white below. Larger size, relatively shorter beak, and lighter coloration distinguish *Ziphius cavirostris* from the somewhat similar *Mesoplodon mirus*.

Measurements.—Adults measure 18-28 feet in length.

General Distribution.—Cosmopolitan.

Distribution in Virginia.—A specimen, U. S. National Museum No. 276656, was obtained August 28, 1944, one mile north of False Cape, Princess Anne County, Virginia, by L. H. Kaltenberger and L. C. Verduin. It should occur more frequently.

Habitat.—All seas.

BIBLIOGRAPHY

The following list of publications contains only those which have been consulted in the preparation of the manuscript, and is not intended to be a complete bibliography of the mammals of Virginia.

ALLEN, GLOVER M. 1941. Pigmy sperm whale in the Atlantic. Zool. Ser. Field Mus. Nat. Hist., vol. 27, pp. 17-37.

.... 1942. Extinct and vanishing mammals of the Western Hemisphere. Amer. Committee for International Wildlife Protection, xv + 620 pp., illus.

ALLEN, HARRISON. 1893. A monograph of the bats of North America. U. S. Nat. Mus. Bull. no. 43, ix + 198 pp., 38 pls.

ALLEN, JOEL A. 1876. The former range of some New England carnivorous mammals. Amer. Nat., vol. 10, pp. 708-715.

.... 1877. History of the American bison, (*Bison americanus*). 9th Ann. Rept. U. S. Geol. and Geogr. Surv. Terr., pt. 3, Zool., pp. 441-587.

.... 1880. History of North American pinnipeds. U. S. Geol. & Geogr. Surv. Terr., Misc. Publ. no. 12, xvi + 785 pp., 60 figs.

ALVORD, CLARENCE W., and LEE BIDGOOD. 1912. The first explorations of the Trans-Allegheny region by the Virginians 1650-1674. 275 pp. Cleveland.

ANONYMOUS. 1899. Virginia game and field sports. Description of them by the botanist Clayton in 1739. Va. Hist. Mag., vol. 7, no. 2, pp. 172-174.

ANTHONY, HAROLD E. 1928. Field book of North American mammals. xxvi + 674 pp., 150 figs., 48 pls. New York and London.

ARBER, EDWARD. 1910. Travels and works of Captain John Smith, president of Virginia and admiral of New England, 1580-1631. cxxxvi + 984 pp.

AUDUBON, JOHN JAMES, and JOHN BACHMAN. 1849-1854. The quadrupeds of North America. Vol. 1, viii + 383 pp., 50 pls.; vol. 2, 335 pp., 50 pls.; vol. 3, 348 pp., 50 pls. New York.

BAILEY, HAROLD H. 1930. Correcting inaccurate ranges of certain Florida mammals and others of Virginia and the Carolinas. The Bailey Mus. and Libr. Nat. Hist. Bull. 5, 4 pp. Miami.

BAILEY, VERNON. 1896. Occurence of the native wood rat at Washington, D. C. Science, vol. 3, no. 69, p. 628.

.... 1900. Revision of American voles of the genus *Microtus*. N. Amer. Fauna, no. 17, 88 pp., 17 figs., 5 pls.

.... 1923. Mammals of the District of Columbia. Proc. Biol. Soc. Wash., vol. 36, pp. 103-138.

.... 1929. Government report of game survey in Bath and Highland Counties. Game and Fish Conservationist, vol. 9, no. 1, pp. 3-6. Va.

BAIRD, SPENCER F. 1859. Mammals of North America; the descriptions of species based chiefly on the collections in the museum of the Smithsonian Institution. Pt. 1, xxxiv + 752, 60 pls. Philadelphia.

BANGS, OUTRAM. 1896. A review of the squirrels of eastern North America. Proc. Biol. Soc. Wash., vol. 10, pp. 145-167, 3 pls.

BARBOUR, THOMAS, and GLOVER M. ALLEN. 1922. The white-tailed deer of the eastern United States. Jour. Mamm., vol. 3, no. 2, pp. 65-78, 2 pls.

BELL, J. M. 1913. Hunting the fleet-footed deer in Virginia. Amer. Field, vol 79, no. 5, p. 98.

BERRY, E. W., and W. K. GREGORY. 1906. *Prorosurarus alleni,* a new genus and species of walrus from the Upper Miocene of Yorktown, Virginia. Amer. Jour. Sci., vol. 21, no. 4, pp. 444-450.

BEVERLY, ROBERT. 1705. The history and present state of Virginia. Book 1, x + 104 pp.; book 2, 4 pp.; book 3, 64 pp.; book 4, 83 pp.; illus.

BOLE, BENJAMIN P., JR., and PHILIP N. MOULTHROP. 1942. The Ohio recent mammal collection in the Cleveland Museum of Natural History. Sci. Publ. Cleveland Mus. Nat. Hist., vol. 5, no. 6, pp. 83-181.

BOYD, WILLIAM K. 1929. William Byrd's histories of the dividing line betwixt Virginia and North Carolina. xxvii + 341 pp. The N. C. Historical Commission, Raleigh.

BROOKS, ALONZO B. 1929. Mammals of West Virginia. The W. Va. Encyclopedia, Ed. 1, xxiv + 1,052 pp. Charleston, W. Va.

BRUCE, JAMES A. 1937. *Sorex longirostris longirostris* in Augusta County, Virginia. Jour. Mamm., vol. 18, no. 4, p. 513.

BURT, WILLIAM H. 1943. Changes in the nomenclature of Michigan mammals. Occ. Papers Mus. Zool. Univ. Mich., no. 481, 9 pp.

CLARK, AUSTIN H. 1939. Some Pleistocene mammals from Warren County, Virginia. The Raven, vol. 10, nos. 4 and 5, pp. 6-7.

CLAYTON, JOHN. 1694. On the beasts and serpents of Virginia. Philos. Trans. Royal Soc. London, vol. 18, no. 210, pp. 121-135.

COPE, EDWIN D. 1868. Observations on the living inhabitants of the caves in southwestern Virginia. Proc. Acad. Nat. Sci. Phila., pp. 85-86.

COTTAM, CLARENCE, ARNOLD L. NELSON, and TALBOTT E. CLARKE. 1939. Notes on early winter food habits of the black bear in George Washington National Forest. Jour. Mamm., vol. 20, no. 3, pp. 310-314.

COUES, ELLIOTT. 1871. Former eastward range of the buffalo. Amer. Nat., vol. 5, pp. 719-720.

.... 1877. Fur-bearing animals: a monograph of North American mustelidae. U. S. Geol. Surv. Terr., Misc. Publ. no. 8, xiv + 348 pp., 20 pls.

.........., and JOEL A. ALLEN. 1877. Monographs of North American rodentia. Rept. U. S. Geol. Surv. Terr., vol. 11, nos. 1-12, x + 1,091 pp., 5 pls.

DEKAY, JAMES E. 1842. Zoology of New York. Part I. Mammalia. xv + 146 pp., 33 pls. Albany.

DENBRIGHT. 1882. Wolves in Virginia. Forest and Stream, vol. 18, p. 189.

DOYLE, WILLIAM E. 1881. History of the buffalo. Amer. Nat., vol 15, pp. 119-124.

DOZIER, HERBERT L., and HAROLD E. HALL. 1944. Observations on the Bryant fox squirrrel *Sciurus niger bryanti* Bailey. Maryland Conservationist, Winter Issue (1944), 12 pp., 7 figs., 1 table.

ELLIOT, DANIEL G. 1901. A synopsis of the mammals of North America and the adjacent Seas. Field Columbian Mus. Zool. Series, vol. 2, pp. xiv + 471, 94 figs., 49 pls.

ELY, ALFRED, et al. 1939. North American big game. xxii + 533 pp., 34 pls., 27 tables. New York and London.

FENNEMAN, NEVIN M. 1938. Physiography of the eastern United States. xiii + 714 pp., 7 pls. New York and London.

GARDNER, MARSHALL C. 1946. A new cotton rat from Virginia. Proc. Biol. Soc. Washington, vol. 59, pp. 137.

GOLDMAN, EDWARD A. 1910. Revision of the wood rats of the genus *Neotoma*. N. Amer. Fauna, No. 31, 124 pp., 8 pls., 14 figs.

.... 1918. The rice rats of North America (Genus *Oryzomys*). N. Amer. Fauna, no. 43, 100 pp., 6 pls., 11 figs.

.... 1937. The wolves of North America. Jour. Mamm., vol. 18, no. 1, pp. 37-45.

GOODE, G. BROWN. 1896. Albemarle in Revolutionary Days. Natl. Geog. Mag., vol. 7, p. 273.

GREENFIELD, RAY. 1938. *Napaeozapus insignis* in Virginia. Jour. Mamm., vol. 19, no. 2, p. 254.

HAMILTON, WILLIAM J., JR. 1943. The mammals of eastern United States. 432 pp., frontis., 184 figs. Ithaca.

.... 1944. The biology of the little short-tailed shrew, *Cryptotis parva*. Jour. Mamm., vol. 25, no. 1, pp. 1-7, 1 pl.

HAY, OLIVER P. 1923. The Pleistocene of North America and its vertebrated animals from the states east of the Mississippi River and from the Canadian Provinces east of longitude 95°. Carnegie Inst. of Wash., Publ. 322, viii + 499 pp., 25 figs., 41 maps.

HOLLISTER, NED. 1911. A systematic synopsis of the muskrats. N. Amer Fauna, no. 32, 47 pp., 6 pls.

HOOPER, EMMET T. 1942. The water shrew (*Sorex palustris*) of the southern Allegheny Mountains. Occ. Papers Mus. Zool. Univ. Mich., no. 463, 4 pp.

.... 1943. Geographic variation in harvest mice of the species *Reithrodontomys humulis*. Occ. Papers Mus. Zool. Univ. Mich., no. 477, 19 pp., 1 map.

.........., and EARL R. CADY. 1941. Notes on certain mammals of the mountains of southwestern Virginia. Jour. Mamm., vol. 22, pp. 323-325.

HORNADAY, WILLIAM T. 1889. The extermination of the American bison, with a sketch of its discovery and life history. Annual Report of the Board of Regents of the Smithsonian Institution for the year ending June 30, 1887, Pt 2, pp. 367-548, 21 pls., map.

HOWELL, A. BRAZIER. 1927. Revision of the American lemming mice (Genus *Synaptomys*). N. Amer. Fauna, no. 50, 37 pp., 2 pls., 11 figs.

HOWELL, ARTHUR H. 1901. Revision of the skunks of the genus *Chincha* (*Mephitis*). N. Amer. Fauna, no. 20, 62 pp., 8 pls.

.... 1906. Revision of the skunks of the genus *Spilogale*. N. Amer. Fauna, no. 26, 55 pp., 10 pls. (incl. 1 map).

.... 1909. Notes on the distribution of certain mammals in the southeastern United States. Proc. Biol. Soc. Wash., vol. 22, pp. 55-68.

.... 1911. Capture of *Sorex dispar* in West Virginia. Proc. Biol. Soc. Wash., vol. 24, pp. 98-99.

.... 1914. Revision of the American harvest mice (Genus *Reithrodontomys*). N. Amer. Fauna, no. 36, 97 pp., 7 pls., 6 figs.

.... 1915. Revision of the American marmots. N. Amer. Fauna, no. 37, 80 pp., 15 pls., 3 figs.

.... 1918. Revision of American flying squirrels. N. Amer. Fauna, no. 44, 64 pp., 7 pls., 4 figs.

.... 1929. Revision of the American chipmunks (Genera *Tamias* and *Eutamias*). N. Amer. Fauna, no. 52, 157 pp., 10 pls., 9 figs.

.... 1939. Description of a new subspecies of the golden mouse. Jour. Mamm., vol. 20, no. 4, p. 498.

HOWLE, T. PETER. 1915. Beaver in the James River. Forest and Stream, vol. 84, p. 229.

JACKSON, HARTLEY H. T. 1915. A review of the American moles. N. Amer. Fauna, no. 38, 100 pp., 6 pls., 27 figs.

.... 1928. A taxonomic review of the American long-tailed shrews (Genera *Sorex* and *Microsorex*). N. Amer. Fauna, no. 51, vi + 238 pp., 13 pls., 24 figs.

JEFFERSON, THOMAS. 1799. A memoir on the discovery of certain bones of a quadruped of the clawed kind in the western parts of Virginia. Trans. Amer. Philos. Soc., vol. 4, pp. 246-260.

.... 1853. Notes on Virginia (written in 1781). J. W. Randolph, Richmond.

JORDAN, DAVID STARR. 1876. Manual of the vertebrates of the northern United States, including the district east of the Mississippi River, and north of North Carolina and Tennessee, exclusive of marine species. 342 pp. Chicago.

KELLOGG, REMINGTON. 1937. Annotated list of West Virginia mammals. Proc. U. S. Nat. Mus., vol. 84, no. 3022, pp. 443-479.

.... 1939. Annotated list of Tennessee mammals. Proc. U. S. Nat. Mus., vol. 86, no. 3051, pp. 245-303.

.... 1939. A new red-backed mouse from Kentucky and Virginia. Proc. Biol. Soc. Wash., vol. 52, pp. 37-40.

.... 1940. Whales, giants of the sea. Natl. Geog. Mag., vol. 77, no. 1, pp. 35-90, 24 pls., 25 figs.

KOMAREK, EDWIN V. 1932. Distribution of *Microtus chrotorrhinus*, with description of a new subspecies. Jour. Mamm., vol. 13, no. 2, pp. 155-158, 1 map, 1 fig.

.........., and ROY KOMAREK. 1938. Mammals of the Great Smoky Mountains. Bull. Chicago Acad. Sciences, vol. 5, no. 6, 162 pp., 6 figs., 1 map.

LEIDY, JOSEPH. 1851. Description of *Balaena palaeatlantica* and *Balaena prisca*, Leidy, based on fragments of fossil bones from the Miocene formation of Virginia. Proc. Acad. Nat. Sci. Phila., vol. 5, pp. 308-309.

.... 1852. Remarks on a fossil Delphinus (*D. conradi*) from the Miocene of Virginia. Proc. Acad. Nat. Sci. Phila., vol. 6, p. 35.

LEWIS, JOHN B. 1927. A mink fight. Jour. Mamm., vol. 8, no. 4, p. 308.

.... 1938. List of mammals observed in Amelia, Brunswick and Norfolk Counties. Unpublished MS., 6 pp.

.... 1940. Mammals of Amelia County, Virginia. Jour. Mamm., vol. 21, no. 4, pp. 422-428.

.... 1941. Porcupine in Virginia. Jour. Mamm., vol. 22, no. 4, p. 452.

.... 1944. Cotton rat in Lower Piedmont Virginia. Jour. Mamm., vol. 25, no. 2, pp. 195-196.

.... 1945. Mammals of the Seward Forest (Va.) and adjacent territory, 1940-1944. Unpublished MS., 9 pp.

LLEWELLYN, LEONARD M. 1942. Notes on the Alleghenian least weasel in Virginia. Jour. Mamm., vol. 23, no. 4, pp. 439-441, 1 table.

.... 1943. A determination of the species and subspecies of the rabbits of the genus *Sylvilagus* and their distribution in Virginia. Unpublished thesis (VPI); 47 pp., 15 figs., 7 tab., frontis.

.........., and C. O. HANDLEY. 1945. The cottontail rabbits of Virginia. Jour. Mamm., vol. 26, no. 4, pp. 379-390, 2 maps, 1 table.

LYON, MARCUS W., JR. 1936. Mammals of Indiana. Amer. Midland Naturalist, vol. 17, no. 1, 384 pp., 125 figs., 85 maps.

MEARNS, EDGAR A. 1911. Description of a new rabbit from islands off the coast of Virginia. Proc. U. S. Nat. Mus., vol. 39, p. 227.

MEARNS, LOUIS Z. 1897. On the occurrence of the genus *Reithrodontomys* in Virginia. Amer. Nat., vol. 31, pp. 160-161.

MERRIAM, C. HART. 1895. Revision of the shrews of the American genera *Blarina* and *Notiosorex*. N. Amer. Fauna, no. 10, 34 pp., 3 pls., 2 figs.

.... 1896. Revision of the lemmings of the genus *Synaptomys,* with descriptions of new species. Proc. Biol. Soc. Wash., vol. 10, pp. 55-64.

.... 1897. Description of a new muskrat from the Great Dismal Swamp, Virginia. Proc. Biol. Soc. Wash., vol. 11, p. 143.

MILLER, GERRIT S., JR. 1897. Revision of the North American bats of the family Vespertilionidae. N. Amer. Fauna, no. 13, 140 pp., 3 pls., 40 figs.

.... 1920. American records of whales of the genus *Pseudorca*. Proc. U. S. Nat. Mus., vol. 57, pp. 205-207.

.... 1924. List of North American recent mammals 1923. U. S. Nat. Mus. Bull. 128, xvi + 673 pp.

.... 1927. A Pollack whale on the coast of Virginia. Proc. Biol. Soc. Wash., vol. 40, pp. 111-112.

.........., and GLOVER M. ALLEN. 1928. The American bats of the genera *Myotis* and *Pizonyx*. Bull. U. S. Nat. Mus., no. 144, viii + 218 pp., 1 pl., 1 fig., 13 maps.

MURRAY, JOSEPH JAMES. 1933. Black bears in Virginia. The Raven, vol. 4, no. 2, p. 9.

NELSON, EDWARD W. 1909. The rabbits of North America. N. Amer. Fauna, no. 29, 314 pp., 13 pls., 19 figs.

.... 1916. The larger North American mammals. Nat. Geogr. Mag., vol. 30, pp. 385-472, col. illus.

.... 1918. Smaller mammals of North America. Nat. Geogr. Mag., vol. 33, pp. 371-493, col. illus.

ODUM, EUGENE P. 1944. *Sorex longirostris* at Mountain Lake, Virginia. Jour. Mamm., vol. 25, no. 2, p. 196.

.... 1944. Notes on small mammal populations at Mountain Lake, Virginia. Jour. Mamm., vol. 25, no. 4, pp. 408-410.

OSGOOD, WILFRED H. 1909. Revision of the mice of the American genus *Peromyscus*. N. Amer. Fauna, no. 28, 285 pp., 8 pls., 12 figs.

PATTON, CLYDE P. 1938. Distributional list of the mammals of Virginia. Unpublished Thesis (VPI), 114 pp., 1 fig.

.... 1939. Distribution notes on certain Virginia mammals. Jour. Mamm., vol. 20, no. 1, pp. 75-77.

.... 1941. The eastern cotton rat in Virginia. Jour. Mamm., vol. 22, no. 1, p. 91.

POOLE, EARL L. 1940. A life history sketch of the Allegheny woodrat. Jour. Mamm., vol. 21, no. 3, pp. 249-270, 3 pls.

.... 1940. The technical name of the Allegheny woodrat. Jour. Mamm., vol. 21, no. 3, pp. 316-318.

.... 1944. The technical names of the northeastern fox squirrels. Jour. Mamm., vol. 25, no. 3, pp. 315-317.

PREBLE, EDWARD A. 1899. Revision of the jumping mice of the genus *Zapus*. N. Amer. Fauna, no. 15, 42 pp., 1 pl., 4 figs.

.... 1910. A new *Microsorex* from the vicinity of Washington, D. C. Proc. Biol. Soc. Wash., vol. 23, pp. 101-102.

REYNARD. 1889. Capturing a whale. Amer. Field, vol. 31, no. 9, pp. 196-198.

ROBINSON, WIRT. 1923. Woodchucks and chipmunks. Jour. Mamm., vol. 4, no. 4, pp. 256-257.

SAYLOR, LAWRENCE W. 1938. Hairy-tailed mole in Virginia. Jour. Mamm., vol. 19, no. 2, p. 247.

SCHORGER, A. WILLIAM. 1944. The validity of *Bison bison pennsylvanicus*. Jour. Mamm., vol. 25, no. 3, pp. 313-315.

SCHWARZ, ERNST, and HENRIETTE K. SCHWARZ. 1943. The wild and commensal stocks of the house mouse, *Mus musculus* Linnaeus. Jour. Mamm., vol. 24, no. 1, pp. 59-72.

SETON, ERNEST THOMPSON. 1929. Lives of game animals 4 vols., illus. Garden City.

STEWART, ROBERT E. 1943. The lemming mouse in Shenandoah Mountains, Virginia. Jour. Mamm., vol. 24, no. 1, p. 104.

STONE, WITMER. 1908. The mammals of New Jersey. Ann. Rep. New Jersey State Mus. for 1907, pp. 33-110.

THORNTON, WILLIAM M. 1896. Spottswood's Expedition of 1716. Natl. Geog. Mag., vol. 7, pp. 265-269.

TRUE, FREDERICK W. 1889. A review of the family Delphinidae. U. S. Nat. Mus. Bull. 36, 191 pp., 47 pls.

WAYLAND, JOHN W. 1912. A history of Rockingham County, Virginia. 473 pp. Dayton, Va.

YOUNG, STANLEY P., and EDWARD A. GOLDMAN. 1944. The wolves of North America. The Amer. Wildlife Inst., Wash., xx + 636 pp., 131 pl., 15 figs., 7 tables.

INDEX

214